Pocket Tables: An Everyday Reference

John O. E. Clark, BSc.
Market House Books, Ltd.

BARNES
&NOBLE
BOOKS
NEW YORK

Pocket Tables: An Everyday Reference

Table of Contents

Table of Contents

Table of Contents

Table of Contents

Table of Contents

Table of Contents

Pocket Tables: An Everyday Reference

1. Mathematical symbols

+	addition sign, positive	$\llcorner$	right angle
−	minus sign, negative	$\angle$	angle
±	plus or minus	∞	infinity
×	multiplication sign, times	%	percentage
÷	division sign, divided by	√	square root
=	equals sign, equals	π	pi
≠	not equal to	∀	for all
~	similar to	Σ	sum
≈	approximately equal to	⇒	implies that
≡	identical to	⇐	is implied by
α	proportional to	{}	encloses a set
>	greater than	∅	empty set
≫	very much greater than	∈	is an element of
≥	greater than or equal to	∉	is not an element of
<	less than	∩	intersection
≪	very much less than	∪	union
≤	less than or equal to	⊂	is a subset of
∴	therefore	⊃	includes the subset
:	ratio	∧	conjunction
⊥	perpendicular to	∨	disjunction

11

2. Number systems

Arabic (decimal)	Binary	Hexadecimal	Roman
1	1	01	I
2	10	02	II
3	11	03	III
4	100	04	IV
5	101	05	V
6	110	06	VI
7	111	07	VII
8	1000	08	VIII
9	1001	09	IX
10	1010	0A	X
20	10100	14	XX
30	11110	1E	XXX
40	101000	28	XL
50	110010	32	L
60	111100	3C	LX
70	1000110	46	LXX
80	1010000	50	LXXX
90	1011010	5A	XC
100	1100100	64	C
500	111110100	1F4	D
1000	1111101000	3E8	M

3. Units of measurement

US standard units

Basic units are the foot (ft), pound (lb), and second (sec).

Linear:

12 inches (in)	= 1 foot (ft)
3 feet (ft)	= 1 yard (yd)
5½ yards (yd)	= 1 pole
22 yards (yd)	= 1 chain (= 4 poles)
220 yards (yd)	= 1 furlong (= 10 chains)
1,760 yards (yd)	= 1 mile (= 8 furlongs = 5,280 feet)

Square:

144 square inches (sq in)	= 1 square foot (sq ft)
9 square feet (sq ft)	= 1 square yard (sq yd)
30¼ square yards (sq yd)	= 1 perch
40 perches	= 1 rood
4 roods	= 1 acre (= 4,840 sq yd)
640 acres	= 1 square mile (sq mile)

Volume:

1,728 cubic inches (cu in)	= 1 cubic foot (cu ft)
27 cubic feet (cu ft)	= 1 cubic yard (cu yd)

Capacity:

4 gills	= 1 pint (= 16 fluid ounces)
2 pints	= 1 quart (= 32 fl oz)
4 quarts	= 1 gallon (= 128 fl oz)
2 gallons	= 1 peck
8 gallons	= 1 bushel (= 4 pecks)
8 bushels	= 1 quarter (= 64 gallons)
1 barrel (oil)	= 42 gallons

Units of measurement

Weight (Avoirdupois):

27.344 grains . . . . = 1 dram (7000 grains = 1 lb)
16 drams . . . . = 1 ounce (oz)
16 ounces (oz) . . . . = 1 pound (lb)
1 hundredweight (cwt) . . . = 100 pounds
20 hundredweight (cwt) . . = 1 ton (= 2,000 pounds)

Metric units

Basic units are the meter (m), kilogram (kg), and second (sec). Other units are formed by adding prefixes, which are also used for forming multiples and submultiples or derived units.

Prefix	Symbol	Example
pico- = x 10^{-12} . . . . .p . . . . pF (picofarad) (million-millionth)		
nano- = x 10^{-9} . . . . .n . . . .ns (nanosecond) (thousand-millionth)		
micro- = x 10^{-6} . . . . .μ . . . .μF (microfarad) (millionth)		
milli- = x 10^{-3} . . . . .m . . .mg (milligram) (thousandth)		
centi- = x 10^{-2} . . . . .c . . . .cm (centimeter) (hundredth)		
deci- = x 10^{-1} . . . . .d . . . .dB (decibel) (tenth)		

Units of measurement

Prefix	Symbol	Example
deca- or deka- = x 10 . . . . (ten times)	da	. . . dam (decameter)
hecto- = x 10^2 . . . . (hundred times)	h	. . . . ha (hectare)
kilo- = x 10^3 . . . . (thousand times)	k	. . . . kW (kilowatt)
mega- = x 10^6 . . . . (million times)	M	. . . MW (megawatt)
giga- = x 10^9 . . . . (thousand million times)	G	. . . GHz (gigahertz)
tera- = x 10^{12} . . . . (million million times)	T	. . . Tm (terameter)

Note: 1 hectare= 100 ares

1 square kilometer = 100 hectares

4. SI units

Base units:

Unit	Symbol	Quantity	Definition
meter	m	length	Distance light travels in a vacuum in 1/299792458 seconds
kilogram	kg	mass	Mass of the international prototype (a cylinder of platinum-iridium alloy)
second	s	time	Time taken for 9,192,631,770 resonance vibrations of an atom of cesium-133
kelvin	K	temperature	1/273.16 of the thermodynamic temperature of the triple point of water
ampere	A	electric current	Current that produces a force of 2×10^{-7} newtons per meter between two parallel conductors of infinite length and negligible cross-section placed 1 meter apart in a vacuum

SI units

Unit	Symbol	Quantity	Definition
mole	mol	amount of substance	Amount of substance that contains as many atoms (or molecules, ions, or subatomic particles) as 12 grams of carbon-12 has atoms
candela	cd	luminous intensity	Luminous intensity of a source that emits monochromatic light of frequency 540×10^{12} hertz of radiant intensity 1/683 watt per steradian in a given direction

Supplementary units:

Unit	Symbol	Quantity	Definition
radian	rad	plane angle	Angle subtended at the center of a circle by an arc whose length is the radius of the circle
steradian	sr	solid angle	Solid angle subtended sphere by a part of the surface whose area is equal to the square of the radius of the sphere

SI units

Derived units:

Unit	Symbol	Quantity	Definition
becquerel	Bq	radioactivity	Activity of a quantity of a radioisotope in which 1 nucleus decays every second (on average)
coulomb	C	electric charge	Charge that is carried by a current of 1 ampere flowing for 1 second
farad	F	electric capacitance	Capacitance that holds a charge of 1 coulomb when it is charged by a potential difference of 1 volt
gray	Gy	absorbed dose	Dosage of ionizing radiation corresponding to 1 joule of energy per kilogram
henry	H	inductance	Mutual inductance in a closed circuit in which an e.m.f. of 1 volt is produced by a current that varies at 1 ampere per second
hertz	Hz	frequency	Frequency of 1 cycle per second

SI units

Unit	Symbol	Quantity	Definition
joule	J	energy	Work done when a force of 1 newton moves its point of application 1 meter in its direction of application
lumen	lm	luminous flux	Amount of light emitted per unit solid angle by a source of 1 candela intensity
lux	lx	illuminance	Amount of light that illuminates 1 square meter with a flux of 1 lumen
newton	N	force	Force that gives a mass of 1 kilogram an acceleration of 1 meter per second per second
ohm	W	electric resistance	Resistance of a conductor across which a potential of 1 volt produces a current of 1 ampere
pascal	Pa	pressure	Pressure exerted when a force of 1 newton acts on an area of 1 square meter

SI units

Unit	Symbol	Quantity	Definition
siemens	S	electric conductance	Conductance of a material or circuit component that has a resistance of 1 ohm
sievert	Sv	dose equivalent	Radiation dosage equal to 1 joule of radiant energy per kilogram
tesla	T	magnetic flux density	Flux density of 1 weber of magnetic flux per square meter
volt	V	electric potential	Potential difference across a conductor in which a constant current of 1 ampere dissipates 1 watt of power
watt	W	power	Amount of power equal to a rate of energy transfer of (or doing work at) 1 joule per second
weber	Wb	magnetic flux	Amount of magnetic flux that, decaying to zero in 1 second, induces an e.m.f. of 1 volt in a circuit of one turn

5. Other measures

Apothecaries' capacity measure:

60 minims	= 1 fluid drachm
8 drachms	= 1 fluid ounce
16 fluid ounces	= 1 pint
8 pints	= 1 gallon

Apothecaries' weights:

20 grains	= 1 scruple
3 scruples	= 1 drachm
8 drachms	= 1 ounce

Nautical measure:

6 feet	= 1 fathom
120 fathoms	= 1 cable (= 720 feet)
6,076 feet	= 1 nautical mile
3 nautical miles	= 1 league (= 3.456 statue miles)
60 nautical miles	= 1 degree (a speed of 1 nautical mile per hour = 1 knot)

Troy weight:

24 grains	= 1 pennyweight
20 pennyweights	= 1 ounce
12 ounces	= 1 pound

Other measures

Household capacity measure:

3 teaspoons	= 1 tablespoon
16 tablespoons	= 1 cup
2 cups	= 1 pint
2 pints	= 1 quart
4 quarts	= 1 gallon

Paper measure:

24 sheets	= 1 quire
20 quires	= 1 ream
1 bundle	= 2 reams

Lumber measure:

1 board foot	= 144 cubic inches
1 cord foot	= 16 cubic feet
1 cord	= 8 cords feet

6. Length, area, and volume

Conversion factors
Standard to metric:

To convert		Multiply by
Length:		
inches	to millimeters	25.4
inches	to centimeters	2.54
inches	to meters	0.254
feet	to centimeters	30.48
feet	to meters	0.3048
yards	to meters	0.9144
miles	to kilometers	1.6093
Area:		
square inches	to square centimeters	6.4516
square feet	to square meters	0.0929
square yards	to square meters	0.8361
square miles	to square kilometers	2.5898
acres	to hectares	0.4047
acres	to square kilometers	0.00405
Volume:		
cubic inches	to cubic centimeters	16.3871
cubic feet	to cubic meters	0.0283
cubic yards	to cubic meters	0.7646
cubic miles	to cubic kilometers	4.1682
Liquid:		
fluid ounces	to milliliters	28.5
pints	to milliliters	473.00
pints	to liters	0.473
gallons	to liters	3.785

Length, area, and volume

To convert		Multiply by
Length:		
millimeters	to inches	0.03937
centimeters	to inches	0.3937
meters	to inches	39.37
meters	to feet	3.2808
meters	to yards	1.0936
kilometers	to miles	0.6214
Area:		
square centimeters	to square inches	0.1552
square meters	to square feet	10.7639
square meters	to square yards	1.196
square kilometers	to square miles	0.3860
square kilometers	to acres	247.10
hectares	to acres	2.4710
Volume:		
cubic centimeters	to cubic inches	0.0610
cubic meters	to cubic feet	35.315
cubic meters	to cubic yards	1.308
cubic kilometers	to cubic miles	0.2399
Capacity:		
milliliters	to fluid ounces	0.0352
milliliters	to pints	0.002114
liters	to pints	2.114
liters	to gallons	0.2642

7. Force, energy, and work

The SI unit of force is the newton, defined as the force that will accelerate a mass of 1 kilogram at a rate of 1 meter per second per second. The corresponding standard unit is the poundal, equal to the force that can accelerate a mass of 1 pound by 1 foot per second per second.

To convert		Multiply by
newtons	to poundals	7.233
poundals	to newtons	0.1383

Table of equivalents:

newtons	poundals	newtons	poundals
1	7.233	35	253.155
2	14.466	40	289.320
3	21.699	45	325.485
4	28.932	50	361.650
5	36.165	55	397.815
6	43.398	60	433.980
7	50.631	65	470.145
8	57.864	70	506.310
9	65.097	75	542.475
10	72.330	80	578.640
15	108.495	85	614.805
20	144.660	90	650.970
25	180.825	95	687.135
30	216.990	100	723.300

Force, energy, and work

Table of equivalents:

poundals	newtons	poundals	newtons
1	0.1383	30	4.149
2	0.277	40	5.532
3	0.415	50	6.915
4	0.553	100	13.83
5	0.692	200	27.66
6	0.830	300	41.49
7	0.968	400	55.32
8	1.106	500	69.15
9	1.245	600	82.98
10	1.383	700	96.81
20	2.766		

Weight is a type of force—caused by the force of gravity. Strictly speaking, therefore, weights should be measured in newtons or poundal (see above for conversions). In everyday use, however, people use units of mass to represent weights, typically kilograms and pounds. These are known scientifically as kilograms-force and pounds-force.

Force applied to an area creates a pressure. Typical units of pressure are newton per square meter (which has a special name, the pascal) and poundals per square foot. Again, in common standard usage, the mass unit is employed and pressures are quoted in pounds per square inch.

To convert		Multiply by
pascals	to poundals per sq ft.	0.672
poundals per sq ft.	to pascals	1.488

Force, energy, and work

Table of equivalents:

pascals	poundals per sq ft.	pascals	poundals per sq ft.
1	0.672	35	23.52
2	1.344	40	26.88
3	2.016	45	30.24
4	2.688	50	33.60
5	3.360	55	36.96
6	4.032	60	40.32
7	4.704	65	43.68
8	5.376	70	47.04
9	6.048	75	50.40
10	6.720	80	53.76
15	10.08	85	57.12
20	13.44	90	60.48
25	16.80	95	63.84
30	20.16	100	67.20

poundals per sq ft.	pascals	poundals per sq ft.	pascals
1	1.488	35	52.09
2	2.976	40	59.53
3	4.464	45	66.97
4	5.953	50	74.41
5	7.441	55	81.85
6	8.929	60	89.29
7	10.42	65	98.22
8	11.91	70	104.17
9	13.39	75	111.61
10	14.88	80	119.05
15	23.32	85	126.49
20	29.76	90	133.93
25	37.20	95	141.38
30	44.64	100	148.82

Force, energy, and work

Energy is the capacity for doing work. Its principal units are the joule (J) [and kilojoule (kJ)], the calorie (cal) and kilocalorie (kcal, sometimes written Cal), generally used for heat measurements, and the little-used foot-pound.

To convert		Multiply by
joules	to calories	0.239
kilojoules	to kilocalories	0.239
calories	to joules	4.187
kilocalories	to kilojoules	4.187

Tables of equivalents:

joules (or kilojoules)	calories (or kilocalories)	joules (or kilojoules)	calories (or kilocalories)
1	0.239	35	8.365
2	0.478	40	9.554
3	0.716	45	10.755
4	0.995	50	11.942
5	1.194	55	13.145
6	1.433	60	14.330
7	1.672	65	15.535
8	1.911	70	16.719
9	2.150	75	17.925
10	2.388	80	19.108
15	3.585	85	20.315
20	4.777	90	21.496
25	5.975	95	22.705
30	7.165	100	23.885

Force, energy, and work

calories (or kilocalories)	joules (or kilojoules)	calories (or kilocalories)	joules (or kilojoules)
1	4.187	35	146.538
2	8.374	40	167.472
3	12.560	45	188.406
4	16.747	50	209.340
5	20.934	55	230.274
6	25.121	60	251.208
7	29.308	65	272.142
8	33.494	70	293.076
9	37.681	75	314.010
10	41.868	80	334.944
15	62.802	85	355.878
20	83.736	90	376.812
25	104.670	95	397.746
30	125.604	100	418.680

The units of work are the same as those of energy. In scientific terms, work is the transfer of energy that occurs when a force causes an object to move in the direction of the force. In the metric system it is generally measured in joules (also called newton-meters, because 1 joule is the energy transferred when a force of 1 newton moves through a distance of 1 meter). The corresponding standard unit is the foot-poundal.

To convert		Multiply by
joules	to foot-poundals	23.734
foot-poundals	to joules	0.0421

Force, energy, and work

Tables of equivalents:

joules	foot-poundals	joules	foot-poundals
1	23.734	35	830.69
2	47.468	40	949.36
3	71.202	45	1068.0
4	94.936	50	1186.7
5	118.67	55	1305.4
6	142.40	60	1424.0
7	166.14	65	1542.7
8	189.87	70	1661.4
9	213.61	75	1780.0
10	237.34	80	1898.7
15	356.01	85	2017.4
20	474.68	90	2136.1
25	593.35	95	2254.7
30	712.02	100	2373.4

foot-poundals	joules	foot-poundals	joules
1	0.0421	30	1.264
2	0.0843	40	1.686
3	0.1264	50	2.107
4	0.1686	100	4.214
5	0.2107	200	8.429
6	0.2528	300	1.264
7	0.2950	400	16.86
8	0.3371	500	21.07
9	0.3793	1000	42.14
10	0.4214	2000	84.28
20	0.8428	3000	126.4

Force, energy, and work

Power is the rate of doing work. In the metric system it is measured in watts (1 watt = 1 joule per second); in the standard system power is measured in horsepower, originally defined as the power needed to lift 33,000 pounds 1 foot in 1 second. A watt is a small unit and so in practice the kilowatt (= 1000 watts) is often employed.

To convert		multiply by
kilowatts	to horsepower	1.341
horsepower	to kilowatts	0.746

Tables of equivalents:

kilowatts	horsepower	kilowatts	horsepower
1	1.341	35	46.935
2	2.682	40	53.641
3	4.023	45	60.345
4	5.354	50	67.051
5	6.705	55	73.755
6	8.046	60	80.461
7	9.387	65	87.165
8	10.728	70	93.871
9	12.069	75	100.575
10	13.410	80	107.280
15	20.115	85	113.985
20	26.820	90	120.690
25	33.525	95	127.395
30	40.231	100	134.100

Force, energy, and work

horsepower	kilowatts	horsepower	kilowatts
1	0.746	35	26.099
2	1.491	40	29.828
3	2.237	45	33.566
4	2.983	50	37.285
5	3.729	55	40.014
6	4.474	60	44.742
7	5.220	65	48.471
8	5.966	70	52.199
9	6.711	75	55.928
10	7.457	80	59.656
15	11.186	85	63.385
20	14.914	90	67.113
25	18.642	95	70.842
30	22.371	100	74.570

8. Temperature scales and conversions

The two most common temperature scales are Fahrenheit (on which water freezes at 32° and boils at 212°) and Celsius (also called Centigrade, on which water freezes at 0° and boils at 100°). Interconversion between the two scales is straightforward if it is remembered that the zeros on the two scales are 32°F apart and that the Fahrenheit scale has 180° between the two fixed points, whereas the Celsius scale has only 100°—i.e. Fahrenheit degrees are 180/100 = 9/5 times "smaller" than Celsius degrees. So, to convert a Fahrenheit temperature to a Celsius:

SUBTRACT 32 AND MULTIPLY BY 5/9

(i.e. after subtracting 32 from the Fahrenheit temperature, multiply by 5 and divide this product by 9—or multiply by 0.556 if using a calculator). To convert a Celsius temperature to Fahrenheit:

MULTIPLY BY 9/5 AND ADD 32

(i.e. multiply by 9 and divide by 5—or multiply by 1.8 if using a calculator—and then add 32 to the result).

Temperature scales and conversions

Conversion table °C to °F:

°C	°F	°C	°F	°C	°F
-200	-328	55	131	250	482
-150	-238	60	140	300	572
-100	-148	65	149	350	662
-50	-58	70	158	400	752
-40	-40	75	167	450	842
-30	-22	80	176	500	932
-20	-4	85	185	550	1022
-10	14	90	194	600	1112
-5	23	95	203	650	1202
0	32	100	212	700	1292
5	41	110	230	750	1382
10	50	120	248	800	1472
15	59	130	266	850	1562
20	68	140	284	900	1652
25	77	150	302	950	1742
30	86	160	320	1000	1832
35	95	170	338	2000	3632
40	104	180	356	3000	5432
45	113	190	374	4000	7232
50	122	200	392	5000	9932

Temperature scales and conversions

Conversion table °F to °C:

°F	°C	°F	°C	°F	°C
-200	-128.89	55	12.78	300	148.89
-150	-101.11	60	15.56	350	176.67
-100	-73.33	65	18.33	400	204.44
-50	-45.56	70	21.11	450	232.22
-40	-40.00	75	23.89	500	260.00
-30	-34.44	80	26.67	550	287.78
-20	-28.89	85	29.44	600	315.56
-10	-23.33	90	32.22	650	343.33
-5	-20.56	95	35.00	700	371.11
0	-17.78	100	37.78	750	398.89
5	-15.00	110	43.33	800	426.67
10	-12.22	120	48.89	850	454.44
15	-9.44	130	54.44	900	482.22
20	-6.67	140	60.00	950	510.00
25	-3.89	150	65.56	1000	537.78
30	-1.11	160	71.11	2000	1093.33
35	1.67	180	82.22	3000	1648.89
40	4.44	190	87.78	4000	2204.44
45	7.22	200	93.33	5000	2760.00
50	10.00	250	121.11	6000	3315.56

9. Other unit conversions

To convert			Multiply by
acre-feet	to	cubic feet	x 3630
	to	gallons	x 3.259 x 10^5
	to	cubic meters	x 1233.5
acres	to	hectares	x 0.405
	to	square chains	x 10
	to	square feet	x 43,560
	to	square kilometers	x 4.047 x 10^{-3}
	to	square yards	x 4840
angstroms	to	centimeters	x 1 x 10^{-8}
	to	inches	x 3.937 x 10^{-9}
astronomical units	to	light-years	x 1.58 x 10^{-5}
atmospheres	to	bars	x 1.1033
	to	kilopascals	x 101.325
bars	to	atmospheres	x 0.906
bytes	to	megabytes	x 9.536 x 10^{-7}
carats	to	grains	x 3.087
	to	grams	x 0.2
centimeters	to	angstroms	x 1 x 10^8
	to	hands	x 0.98
centimeters per hour	to	inches per minute	x 6.56 x 10^{-3}

Other unit conversions

To convert			Multiply by
centimeters per sec	to	inches per second	x 0.394
chains	to	feet	x 66
	to	meters	x 20.116
	to	yards	x 22
cubic centimeters	to	pints	x 2.113 x10^{-3}
cubic feet	to	acre-feet	x 2.754 x 10^{-4}
cubic feet per minute	to	liters per minute	x 28.329
cubic inches	to	pints	x 0.0346
cubic meters	to	acre-feet	x 8.107 x 10^{-4}
degrees	to	radians	x 0.0175
dynes	to	joules per centimeter	x 1 x10^{-7}
	to	newtons	x 1 x 10^{-5}
	to	poundals	x 7.233 x 10^{-5}
fathoms	to	meters	x 1.829
feet	to	chains	x 0.015
feet per hour	to	inches per minute	x 0.2
	to	meters per hour	x 0.305
feet per minute	to	meters per minute	x 0.305

Other unit conversions

To convert			Multiply by
feet per second	to	meters per second	x 0.305
	to	miles per hour	x 0.682
	to	miles per minute	x 1.136 x 10^{-2}
furlongs	to	meters	x 201.168
gallons	to	acre-feet	x 3.060 x 10^{-6}
gallons per minute	to	liters per minute	x 3.785
grains	to	carats	x 0.324
	to	grams	x 0.065
grams	to	carats	x 200
	to	grains	x 15.432
	to	troy ounces	x 0.032
hands	to	centimeters	x 10.16
	to	inches	x 4
hectares	to	acres	x 2.471
	to	square miles	x 0.0039
horsepower	to	kilowatts	x 0.746
inches	to	angstroms	x 2.54 x 10^8
	to	hands	x 0.25
inches per minute	to	centimeters per hour	x 152.4
	to	feet per hour	x 5

Other unit conversions

To convert			Multiply by
inches per second	to	centimeters per sec	x 2.54
joules	to	kilowatt-hours	x 2.77 x 10^{-5}
joules per centimeter	to	dynes	x 1 x 10^{7}
kilogram-force	to	newtons	x 9.807
kilograms per sq cm	to	pounds per sq in	x 14.223
kilometers	to	astronomical units	x 1.057 x 10^{-13}
	to	nautical miles	x 0.54
kilometers per hour	to	feet per minute	x 54.659
	to	knots	x 0.540
	to	meters per second	x 0.278
	to	meters per minute	x 16.667
	to	miles per hour	x 0.621
kilometers per liter	to	miles per gallon	x 2.352
kilopascals	to	atmosphere	x 9.87 x 10^{-3}
kilowatt-hours	to	joules	x 3.6 x 10^{6}
kilowatts	to	horsepower	x 1.341

Other unit conversions

To convert			Multiply by
knots	to	kilometers per hour	x 1.852
	to	miles per hour	x 1.151
light-years	to	astronomical units	x 63,240
	to	kilometers	x 9.461 x 10^{12}
	to	miles	x 5.879 x 10^{12}
	to	parsecs	x 0.307
liters per minute	to	cubic feet per minute	x 0.0353
	to	gallons per minute	x 0.2642
megabytes	to	bytes	x 1,048,576
meters	to	chains	x 0.0497
	to	fathoms	x 0.547
	to	furlongs	x 0.005
meters per hour	to	feet per hour	x 3.2808
meters per minute	to	feet per minute	x 3.281
	to	yards per minute	x 0.914
meters per second	to	feet per second	x 3.281
	to	kilometers per hour	x 3.599
metric tons	to	tons	x 1.1023
miles	to	light-years	x 1.701 x 10^{-13}

Other unit conversions

To convert			Multiply by
miles	to	nautical miles	x 0.869
miles per gallon	to	kilometers per liter	x 0.425
miles per hour	to	feet per second	x 1.467
	to	kilometers per hour	x 1.609
	to	knots	x 0.869
miles per minute	to	feet per second	x 88
nautical miles	to	kilometers	x 1.852
	to	miles	x 1.1508
newtons	to	dynes	x 1 x 10^5
	to	kilogram-force	x 0.10197
	to	poundals	x 7.233
ounces	to	troy ounces	x 0.911
parsecs	to	light-years	x 3.262
pints	to	cubic centimeters	x 473.177
	to	cubic inches	x 28.875
poundals	to	dynes	x 13,820
	to	newtons	x 0.138
pounds per sq in	to	kilograms per sq cm	x 0.070
radians	to	degrees	x 57.31

Other unit conversions

To convert			Multiply by
radians per second	to	revolutions per minute	x 9.5493
revolutions per minute	to	radians per second	x 0.1047
square chains	to	acres	x 0.1
	to	square meters	x 404.686
square feet	to	acres	x 2.29 x 10^{-5}
square kilometers	to	acres	x 247.1
square meters	to	square chains	x 0.0025
square miles	to	hectares	x 259.0
square yards	to	acres	x 2.066 x 10^{-4}
tons	to	metric tons	x 0.9072
troy ounces	to	grams	x 31.103
	to	ounces	x 1.097
yards	to	chains	x 0.045
yards per minute	to	meters per minute	x 1.094

10. Fractions, decimals, and percentages

Fraction	Decimal (to 3 places)	Percentage	Fraction	Decimal (to 3 places)	Percentage
1/64	0.016	1.56%	9/32	0.281	28.13%
1/32	0.031	3.13%	2/7	0.286	28.58%
3/64	0.047	4.69%	19/64	0.297	29.69%
1/20	0.050	5.00%	5/16	0.313	31.25%
1/16	0.063	6.25%	21/64	0.328	32.81%
5/64	0.078	7.81%	1/3	0.333	33.33%
1/12	0.083	8.33%	11/32	0.343	34.38%
1/11	0.091	9.09%	7/20	0.350	35.00%
3/32	0.094	9.38%	23/64	0.359	35.94%
7/64	0.109	10.94%	4/11	0.363	36.36%
1/9	0.111	11.11%	3/8	0.375	37.50%
1/8	0.125	12.5%	25/64	0.391	39.06%
9/64	0.141	14.06%	2/5	0.400	40.00%
1/7	0.143	14.29%	12/32	0.406	40.63%
3/20	0.150	15.00%	5/12	0.417	41.67%
5/32	0.156	15.63%	27/64	0.422	42.19%
1/6	0.167	16.67%	7/16	0.438	43.75%
11/64	0.172	17.19%	29/64	0.422	42.19%
2/11	0.182	18.18%	3/7	0.429	42.86%
3/16	0.188	18.75%	4/9	0.444	44.44%
1/5	0.200	20.00%	5/11	0.455	44.45%
13/64	0.203	20.31%	9/20	0.450	45.00%
7/32	0.219	21.88%	15/32	0.469	46.88%
2/9	0.222	22.22%	31/64	0.484	48.44%
15/64	0.234	23.44%	1/2	0.500	50.00%
1/4	0.250	25.00%	33/64	0.516	51.56%
17/64	0.266	26.56%	17/32	0.531	53.13%
3/11	0.273	27.27%	35/64	0.547	54.69%

Fractions, decimals, and percentages

Fraction	Decimal (to 3 places)	Percentage	Fraction	Decimal (to 3 places)	Percentage
17/32	0.531	53.13%	49/64	0.766	76.56%
6/11	0.545	54.54%	7/9	0.778	77.78%
35/64	0.547	54.69%	25/32	0.781	78.13%
11/20	0.550	55.00%	51/64	0.797	79.69%
9/16	0.562	56.25%	4/5	0.800	80.00%
4/7	0.571	57.14%	13/16	0.812	81.25%
37/64	0.578	57.81%	9/11	0.818	81.81%
7/12	0.583	58.33%	53/64	0.828	82.81%
19/32	0.594	59.37%	5/6	0.833	83.33%
3/6	0.600	60.00%	27/32	0.844	84.38%
39/64	0.609	60.94%	17/20	0.850	85.00%
5/8	0.625	62.50%	6/7	0.857	85.71%
7/11	0.636	63.63%	55/64	0.859	85.94%
41/64	0.641	64.06%	7/8	0.875	87.50%
13/20	0.650	65.00%	8/9	0.889	88.89%
21/32	0.656	65.63%	57/64	0.891	89.06%
2/3	0.667	66.67%	29/32	0.906	90.63%
43/64	0.672	67.19%	10/11	0.909	90.90%
11/16	0.688	68.75%	11/12	0.917	91.67%
45/64	0.703	70.31%	59/64	0.922	92.19%
5/7	0.714	71.43%	15/16	0.938	93.75%
23/32	0.719	71.88%	19/20	0.950	95.00%
8/11	0.727	72.72%	61/64	0.953	95.31%
47/64	0.734	73.44%	31/32	0.969	96.88%
3/4	0.750	75.00%	63/64	0.984	98.44%

11. Squares and square roots

Number	Square	Square root	Number	Square	Square root
1	1	1.000	21	441	4.583
2	4	1.414	22	484	4.690
3	9	1.732	23	529	4.796
4	16	2.000	24	576	4.899
5	25	2.236	25	625	5.000
6	36	2.449	26	676	5.099
7	49	2.646	27	729	5.196
8	64	2.828	28	784	5.292
9	81	3.000	29	841	5.385
10	100	3.162	30	900	5.477
11	121	3.317	31	961	5.568
12	144	3.464	32	1024	5.657
13	169	3.606	33	1089	5.745
14	196	3.742	34	1156	5.831
15	225	3.873	35	1225	5.916
16	256	4.000	36	1296	6.000
17	289	4.123	37	1369	6.083
18	324	4.243	38	1444	6.164
19	361	4.359	39	1521	6.245
20	400	4.472	40	1600	6.325

Squares and square roots

Number	Square	Square root	Number	Square	Square root
41	1681	6.403	71	5041	8.426
42	1764	6.481	72	5184	8.485
43	1849	6.557	73	5329	8.544
44	1936	6.633	74	5476	8.602
45	2025	6.708	75	5625	8.660
46	2116	6.782	76	5776	8.718
47	2209	6.856	77	5929	8.775
48	2304	6.928	78	6084	8.832
49	2401	7.000	79	6241	8.888
50	2500	7.071	80	6400	8.944
51	2601	7.141	81	6561	9.000
52	2704	7.211	82	6724	9.055
53	2809	7.280	83	6889	9.110
54	2916	7.348	84	7056	9.165
55	3025	7.416	85	7225	9.220
56	3136	7.483	86	7396	9.274
57	3249	7.550	87	7569	9.327
58	3364	7.616	88	7744	9.381
59	3481	7.681	89	7921	9.434
60	3600	7.746	90	8100	9.487
61	3721	7.810	91	8281	9.539
62	3844	7.874	92	8464	9.592
63	3969	7.937	93	8649	9.644
64	4096	8.000	94	8836	9.695
65	4225	8.062	95	9025	9.747
66	4356	8.124	96	9216	9.798
67	4489	8.185	97	9409	9.849
68	4624	8.246	98	9604	9.899
69	4761	8.307	99	9801	9.950
70	4900	8.367	100	10,000	10.000

12. Cubes and cube roots

Number	Cube	Cube root	Number	Cube	Cube root
1	1	1.000	21	9261	2.759
2	8	1.260	22	10,648	2.802
3	27	1.442	23	12,167	2.844
4	64	1.587	24	13,824	2.884
5	125	1.710	25	15,625	2.924
6	216	1.817	26	17,576	2.962
7	343	1.913	27	19,683	3.000
8	512	2.000	28	21,952	3.037
9	729	2.080	29	24,389	3.072
10	1000	2.154	30	27,000	3.107
11	1331	2.224	31	29,791	3.141
12	1728	2.289	32	32,768	3.173
13	2197	2.351	33	35,937	3.208
14	2744	2.410	34	39,304	3.240
15	3375	2.466	35	42,875	3.271
16	4096	2.520	36	46,656	3.302
17	4913	2.571	37	50,653	3.332
18	5832	2.621	38	54,872	3.362
19	6859	2.668	39	59,319	3.391
20	8000	2.714	40	64,000	3.420

Cubes and cube roots

Number	Cube	Cube root	Number	Cube	Cube root
41	68,921	3.448	71	357,911	4.141
42	74,088	3.476	72	373,248	4.160
43	79,507	3.503	73	389,017	4.179
44	85,184	3.530	74	405,224	4.198
45	91,125	3.557	75	421,875	4.217
46	97,336	3.583	76	438,976	4.236
47	103,823	3.609	77	456,533	4.254
48	110,592	3.634	78	474,552	4.273
49	117,649	3.659	79	493,039	4.291
50	125,000	3.684	80	512,000	4.309
51	132,651	3.708	81	531,441	4.327
52	140,608	3.733	82	551,368	4.344
53	148,877	3.756	83	571,787	4.362
54	157,464	3.780	84	592,704	4.380
55	166,375	3.803	85	614,125	4.397
56	175,616	3.826	86	636,056	4.414
57	185,193	3.849	87	658,503	4.431
58	195,112	3.871	88	681,472	4.448
59	205,379	3.893	89	704,963	4.465
60	216,000	3.915	90	729,000	4.481
61	226,981	3.936	91	753,571	4.498
62	238,328	3.958	92	778,688	4.514
63	250,047	3.979	93	804,357	4.531
64	262,144	4.000	94	830,584	4.547
65	274,625	4.021	95	857,375	4.563
66	287,496	4.041	96	884,736	4.579
67	300,763	4.062	97	912,673	4.595
68	314,432	4.082	98	941,192	4.610
69	328,509	4.102	99	970,299	4.626
70	343,000	4.121	100	1,000,000	4.642

13. Multiplication table

	Column 1	2	3	4	5	6	7	8	9	10	11	12
Row 1	1	2	3	4	5	6	7	8	9	10	11	12
2	2	4	6	8	10	12	14	16	18	20	22	24
3	3	6	9	12	15	18	21	24	27	30	33	36
4	4	8	12	16	20	24	28	32	36	40	44	48
5	5	10	15	20	25	30	35	40	45	50	55	60
6	6	12	18	24	30	36	42	48	54	60	66	72
7	7	14	21	28	35	42	49	56	63	70	77	84
8	8	16	24	32	40	48	56	64	72	80	88	96
9	9	18	27	36	45	54	63	72	81	90	99	108
10	10	20	30	40	50	60	70	80	90	100	110	120
11	11	22	33	44	55	66	77	88	99	110	121	132
12	12	24	36	48	60	72	84	96	108	120	132	144

14. Geometrical shapes and formulae

Figure	Dimensions
circle	radius r
cone	base radius r, height h, slant height l
cylinder	radius r, height h
ellipse	axes a and b
kite	diagonals a and b
parallelogram	sides a and b height (distance between a sides) h
rectangle	sides a and b
sphere	radius r
square	side a
trapezoid	sides a and b, height h
triangle	base a, height h (other sides b and c)

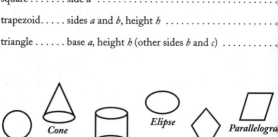

Circle   Cone   Cylinder   Elipse   Kite   Parallelogra

Area	Volume	Perimeter
..πr^2		.$2\pi r$
..πrl	.$\pi r^2 h/3$	
..$2\pi r(h+r)$	.$\pi r^2 h$	
..πab		.$2\pi\sqrt{[(a^2+b^2)/2]}$
..$^1\!/_2 a \times b$		
..$a \times h$		.$2(a+b)$
..$a \times b$		.$2(a+b)$
..$4\pi r^2$	.$4\pi r^3/3$	
..a^2		.$4a$
..$^1\!/_2 h(a+b)$		
..$^1\!/_2 ah$		.$a+b+c$

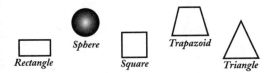

Rectangle   Sphere   Square   Trapazoid   Triangle

15. Earth data

Radius at equator	6378 km (3963 miles)
Radius at poles	6357 km (3950 miles)
Circumference at equator	40,079 km (24,900 miles)
Circumference at poles	40,009 km (24,857 miles)
Surface area	5.095×10^8 sq km (1.967×10^8 sq miles)
Volume	1.083×10^{12} cu km (2.598×10^{11} cu miles)
Mass	5.976×10^{24} kg (6.587×10^{21} tons)
Average density	5.517 gm/cu cm (344 lb/cu ft)
Gravity at equator	9.78 kg/sec/sec (21.561 lb/sec/sec)
Escape velocity	11.2 km/sec (6.960 miles/sec)
Average land elevation	623 meters (2044 ft)
Average ocean depth	3,800 meters (12,467 ft)
Average distance to Sun	1.496×10^8 km ($9,296 \times 10^7$ miles)
Average velocity round Sun	29.77 km/sec (18.50 miles/sec)
Average period of rotation	23 hr 56 min 4 sec

16. Composition of the Earth's crust

Element	Percentage by volume
oxygen	46.6
silicon	27.7
aluminum	8.2
iron	5.0
calcium	4.1
sodium	2.8
potassium	2.6
magnesium	2.1
titanium	0.44
hydrogen	0.114

Composition of the oceans

Element	Percentage by volume
chlorine	1.940
sodium	1.080
magnesium	0.130
sulfur	0.090
calcium	0.041
potassium	0.039
bromine	0.007
carbon	0.003

Composition of the Earth's crust

Abundance of elements in the Earth's crust

Element*	Abundance in parts per million	Element*	Abundance in parts per million
aluminum	82,000	manganese	1000
argon	1.2	molybdenum	1.5
arsenic	1.5	neodymium	38
barium	500	nickel	80
beryllium	2.6	niobium	20
boron	10	nitrogen	25
cesium	3.0	oxygen	470,000
calcium	41,000	phosphorus	1000
carbon	480	potassium	21,000
cerium	68	praseodymium	9.5
chlorine	130	rhodium	90
chromium	100	samarium	8.0
cobalt	20	scandium	16
copper	50	silicon	280,000
dysprosium	6.0	sodium	23,000
erbium	4.0	strontium	370
europium	2.0	sulfur	260
fluorine	950	tantalum	2.0
gadolinium	8.0	terbium	1.0
gallium	18	thorium	12
germanium	2.0	tin	2.0
hafnium	5.3	titanium	6.0
holmium	1.4	tungsten	1.0
hydrogen	1500	uranium	2.0
iron	41,000	vanadium	160
lanthanum	32	ytterbium	3.0
lead	14	yttrium	30
lithium	20	zinc	75
magnesium	23,000	zirconium	190

* elements with more than 1 part per million

17. Composition of the Earth's atmosphere

Component	Percentage by volume
nitrogen	78.09
oxygen	20.95
argon	0.93
carbon dioxide	0.03
neon	0.002
krypton	0.0001
helium	0.0005
methane	0.0003
hydrogen	0.00005
nitrous oxide	0.00005
ozone	0.000004
xenon	0.000009

18. Layers of the atmosphere

Layer	Height above sea level		Characteristics
	km	miles	
troposphere	0–12	0–8	where weather occurs; contains dust and water vapor
stratosphere	12–55	8–34	ozone layer toward the top level
mesosphere	55–80	34–50	sunlight causes chemical reactions
thermosphere	80–400	48–250	temperature steadily rises with height
exosphere	over 400	over 250	hydrogen and helium escape into space

19. Composition of sea water

Element	Percentage by volume
oxygen	85.7
hydrogen	10.7
chlorine	1.94
sodium	1.08
magnesium	0.13
sulfur	0.090
calcium	0.041
potassium	0.039
bromine	0.0070
carbon	0.0028
strontium	0.0008
boron	0.0005

20. Wind-chill factor

To find the wind-chill factor, read off the outside temperature along the top line and read down the column to the line with the measured wind speed. The two lines cross at the wind-chill factor.

Wind speed (mph)	Measured outside temperature (°F)									
	25	20	15	10	5	0	-5	-10	-15	-20
0	25	20	15	10	5	0	-5	-10	-15	-20
5	48	16	11	6	1	-5	-10	-16	-21	-26
10	10	4	-3	-9	-15	-21	-27	-33	-40	-46
15	2	-5	-12	-19	-25	-32	-39	-45	-52	-59
20	-3	-10	-18	-25	-32	-39	-46	-53	-60	-67
25	-7	-15	-22	-30	-37	-45	-52	-60	-67	-74
30	-10	-18	-25	-33	-41	-48	-56	-64	-71	-79
35	-12	-20	-28	-36	-43	-51	-59	-67	-75	-82
40	-14	-22	-29	-37	-45	-53	-61	-69	-77	-85
45	-15	-23	-31	-39	-47	-55	-63	-71	-79	-86

21. Heat-humidity index

To find the heat-humidity index, read off the measured outside temperature down the left-hand column and then read across to the column with the observed percentage humidity. The point of intersection is the heat-humidity index.

Measured temp (°F)	Percentage relative humidity								
	10	20	30	40	50	60	70	80	90
70	65	66	67	68	69	70	70	71	71
75	70	72	73	74	75	76	77	78	79
80	75	77	78	79	81	82	85	86	88
85	80	82	84	86	88	90	93	97	102
90	85	87	90	93	96	100	106	112	122
95	90	93	96	101	107	114	124	135	
100	95	99	104	110	120	132	144		
105	100	105	113	123	135	150			
110	105	112	123	137	150				

22. Geological time scale

Era	Period	Epoch	Approx. time began (million years ago)
Cenozoic	Quaternary	Holocene	0.01
		Pleistocene	1.6
	Tertiary	Pliocene	5.2
		Miocene	23.5
		Oligocene	35.5
		Eocene	56.5
		Paleocene	65
Mesozoic	Cretaceous		145
	Jurassic		210
	Triassic		245
Paleozoic	Permian		290
	Carboniferous		360
	Devonian		410
	Silurian		440
	Ordovician		510
	Cambrian		570
Precambrian	Proterozoic		2500
	Archaean		4600

23. Scientific scales

Beaufort wind scale:

Force	Description	Characteristics	Wind speed (kph/mph)
0	calm	smoke goes straight up; sea surface like a mirror	0–2/0–1.2
1	light air	smoke follows wind direction; ripples on sea surface	1–5/1–3
2	light breeze	wind felt on face, leaves rustle; small wavelets on sea	6–11/4–7
3	gentle breeze	flags flutter, leaves move constantly; wave crests break	13–20/8–12
4	moderate	loose paper blows about, branches sway; small waves, breeze often with "white horses"	20–29/13–18
5	fresh breeze	small trees sway, leaves blown off; moderate waves, many "white horses," some spray	30–39/19–24
6	strong breeze	whistling in phone wires, umbrella hard to hold; large waves with white crests; spray	40–50/25–31
7	moderate gale	large trees move, hard to walk; sea leaps up, spray from breaking waves blows along in the wind	51–61/32–38
8	gale	twigs break off trees; moderatelyhigh waves, crests break into foam that streaks out with the wind	62–74/39–46

Scientific scales

Force	Description	Characteristics	Wind speed (kph/mph)
9	strong gale	branches break off trees, chimney pots and tiles blow off; high waves, crests topple and roll over	75–87/47–54
10	storm	trees uprooted, unstable buildings collapse; very high waves with overhanging crests, surface becomes white, spray affects visibility	88–102/55–63
11	violent storm	widespread damage; extremely high waves, sea covered in white patches of foam along wind direction, spray affects visibility	103–120/64–75
12	hurricane	massive structural damage; air filled with spray and foam, sea white all over; driving spray, very poor visibility	over 120 (75)

Saffir-Simpson scale:

Category of hurricanes	Maximum Sustained Wind Speed mph (m/s)	Minimum Surface Pressure mb	Storm Surge m (ft)
1	74-96 (33-42)	> 980	1.0-1.7 (3-5)
2	97-111 (43-49)	979-965	1.8-2.6 (6-8)
3	112-131 (50-58)	964-945	2.7-3.8 (9-12)
4	132-155 (59-69)	944-920	3.9-5.6 (13-18)
5	156+ (70+)	< 920	5.7+ (19+)

Scientific scales

Mohs' hardness scale:

Mineral	Hardness	Can be scratched by
talc	1.0	fingernail
gypsum	2.0	fingernail
calcite	3.0	copper coin
fluorite	4.0	glass
apatite	5.0	penknife blade
feldspar	6.0	quartz
quartz	7.0	steel file
topaz	8.0	corundum
corundum	9.0	diamond
diamond	10.0	

Hardness of common gemstones:

Gemstone	Hardness	Color
lapis lazuli	5.5	dark blue
opal	6.0	white, orange, rainbow, black
turquoise	6.0	light blue
garnet	6.5	red, pink, green
amethyst	7.0	violet
citrine	7.0	yellow
aquamarine	7.5	green-blue, light blue
beryl	7.5	blue, green, pink
emerald	7.5	green
topaz	8.0	yellow, green, blue, pink, clear
ruby	9.0	red
sapphire	9.0	dark blue, light blue
diamond	10.0	clear, various tints

Scientific scales

Mercalli earthquake scale:

Level	Typical effects in built-up areas
I	not felt by people; detected by seismographs
II	felt by a few people, especially on upper stories; hanging objects swing
III	felt by people indoors, especially on upper stories; stationary cars may rock slightly; vibrations like a passing truck
IV	felt by most people indoors and some outdoors; dishes and windows rattle; stationary cars rock
V	felt by nearly everybody; sleeping people awakened; unstable objects may fall; some dishes and windows broken
VI	felt by everybody; some heavy furniture moved; some plaster falls; trees shake; slight damage
VII	difficult to stand up; some chimneys and loose tiles fall; plaster cracks and falls
VIII	cars difficult to steer; heavy furniture overturned; chimneys, smoke stacks and monuments fall; tree branches break; partial collapse of ordinary buildings
IX	people tend to panic; severe damage to buildings; underground pipes and foundations break
X	most buildings totally collapse; bridges destroyed; water thrown out of lakes and rivers
XI	very few buildings left standing; railroad tracks bent; canals and rivers burst their banks
XII	total destruction; large masses of rock displaced; objects thrown into the air

Scientific scales

Richter earthquake scale:

Level	Increase in magnitude	Relative energy release	Equivalent of TNT
1	1	1	0.170 kg
2	x 10	30	6 kg
3	x 100	960	180 kg
4	x 1000	30,000	5 metric tons
5	x 10,000	920,000	180 metric tons
6	x 100,000	29,000,000	5,650 metric tons
7	x 1,000,000	890,000,000	180,000 metric tons
8	x 10,000,000	28,000,000,000	5,650,000 metric tons

24. Earthquakes of over 7 on Richter scale (since 1980)

Year	Location	Richter level	No. of people killed
1980	Algeria	7.7	3,000
1980	Italy	7.2	4,800
1985	Mexico	8.1	5,000
1988	Armenia	n/a	55,000
1988	China	7.6	1,000
1989	San Francisco	7.1	62
1990	Iran	7.7	50,000
1990	Philippines	7.7	1,650
1991	Georgia (ex-USSR)	7.2	100
1992	Indonesia	7.5	2,500
1993	Japan	7.8	200
1995	Japan	7.2	53,800
1995	Russia	7.6	2,000
1995	Mexico	7.6	70
1995	Taiwan	7.6	2,250
1996	Indonesia	7.5	110
1997	Pakistan	7.3	100
1997	Iran	7.1	1,600
1999	Turkey	7.4	30,000
2001	India	7.9	30,000

25. Continents and areas

Continent	Area (1000 sq km)	Area (1000 sq miles)
Africa	30,295	11,695
Antarctica	13,975	5395
Asia	44,495	17,180
Europe	10,245	3955
North America	24,455	9440
Australasia	8945	3455
South America	17,840	6890

26. World population

Year	Estimated world population (millions)	Year	Estimated world population (millions)
AD 1	180	1960	3,000
1000	275	1970	3,700
1250	375	1980	4,400
1500	420	1985	4,800
1700	615	1990	5,300
1750	750	1994	5,700
1800	900	1996	5,800
1850	1,250	1998	5,900
1900	1,600	2000	6,000
1920	1,900	2015	7,300
1940	2,300	2025	8,500
1950	2,500	2050	9,800

Population milestones:

World population	Year	Comment
1 billion	1805	
2 billion	1927	population doubled in 122 years
3 billion	1960	
4 billion	1974	population doubled again after 47 years
5 billion	1987	
6 billion	2000	
7 billion	2012	
8 billion	2020	population will double again after 46 years

World population

Population growth by continent:

Continent	yearly increase 1950-1994 (%)	yearly increase 1995-2000 (%)	Population in 2000 (est.)
Africa	2.62	2.8	804,500,000
Asia	2.01	1.6	3,728,500,000
Australasia	1.30	1.3	23,100,000
Europe	0.64	0.3	738,200,000
North America	1.27	0.9	306,100,000
Oceania	1.74	1.7	10,700,000
South America	2.38	1.6	344,000,000

27. World nations, areas, and populations

Nation	Area (sq km)	Area (sq miles)	Population*
Afghanistan	652,090	251,775	23,738,000
Albania	28,750	11,100	3,293,000
Algeria	2,381,740	919,595	29,476,000
Andorra	455	175	64,600
Angola	1,246,700	481,355	10,624,000
Antigua and Barbuda	440	170	64,500
Argentina	2,780,400	1,073,520	35,409,000
Armenia	29,800	11,505	3,733,000
Australia	7,713,365	2,978,145	18,508,000
Austria	83,855	32,375	8,087,000
Azerbaijan	86,600	33,435	7,617,000
Bahamas	13,880	5360	287,000
Bahrain	680	260	620,000
Bangladesh	144,000	55,600	125,340,000
Barbados	430	165	265,000
Belarus	207,600	80,155	10,360,000

World nations, areas, and populations

Nation	Area (sq km)	Area (sq miles)	Population*
Belgium	30,520	11,785	10,189,000
Belize	22,965	8865	228,000
Benin	112,620	43,485	5,902,000
Bhutan	47,000	18,145	860,000
Bolivia	1,098,580	424,165	7,186,000
Bosnia-Herzegovina	51,130	19,740	3,124,000
Botswana	581,730	224,605	1,501,000
Brazil	8,512,000	3,286,500	159,691,000
Brunei	5765	2225	308,000
Bulgaria	110,910	42,825	8,329,000
Burkina Faso	274,000	105,790	10,891,000
Burundi	27,834	10,745	6,053,000
Cambodia	181,035	69,900	10,600,000
Cameroon	475,440	183,570	14,678,000
Canada	9,970,610	3,849,675	30,287,000
Cape Verde	4035	1555	394,000

World nations, areas, and populations

Nation	Area (sq km)	Area (sq miles)	Population*
Central African Rep.	622,985	240,535	3,342,000
Chad	1,284,000	495,755	7,166,000
Chile	756,945	292,260	14,376,000
China	9,596,960	3,705,410	1,227,740,000
Colombia	1,138,915	439,735	36,200,000
Comoros	2235	865	514,000
Congo, Dem. Rep. of	2,344,860	905,355	46,674,000
Congo, Rep. of	342,000	132,045	2,583,000
Costa Rica	51,100	19,730	3,468,000
Cote d'Ivoire	322,465	124,505	14,986,000
Croatia	56,540	21,830	4,774,000
Cuba	110,860	42,805	11,190,000
Cyprus	9250	3570	765,000
Czech Republic	78,865	30,450	10,307,000

World nations, areas, and populations

Nation	Area (sq km)	Area (sq miles)	Population*
Denmark	43,075	16,630	5,284,000
Djibouti	23,200	8960	622,000
Dominica	750	290	74,500
Dominican Republic	48,735	18,815	7,802,000
Ecuador	283,560	109,485	11,937,000
Egypt	1,001,450	386,660	62,110,000
El Salvador	21,040	8125	5,662,000
Equatorial Guinea	28,050	10,830	443,000
Eritrea	117,600	45,405	3,590,000
Estonia	45,100	17,415	1,463,000
Ethiopia	1,104,300	426,375	58,733,000
Fiji	18,275	7055	778,000
Finland	338,145	130,560	5,145,000
France	551,500	212,935	58,616,000
Gabon	267,665	103,345	1,190,000
Gambia	11,295	4360	1,248,000

World nations, areas, and populations

Nation	Area (sq km)	Area (sq miles)	Population*
Georgia	69,700	26,910	5,377,000
Germany	356,735	137,735	82,143,000
Ghana	238,535	92,100	17,434,000
Greece	131,990	50,960	10,541,000
Grenada	345	135	98,500
Guatemala	108,890	42,040	11,242,000
Guinea	245,855	94,925	7,405,000
Guinea-Bissau	36,125	13,950	1,179,000
Guyana	214,970	83,000	773,000
Haiti	27,750	10,715	6,611,000
Honduras	112,090	43,275	5,823,000
Hungary	93,030	35,920	10,157,000
Iceland	103,000	39,770	271,000
India	3,287,590	1,269,345	967,613,000
Indonesia	1,919,320	741,050	199,544,000
Iran	1,648,000	636,295	62,304,000

World nations, areas, and populations

Nation	Area (sq km)	Area (sq miles)	Population*
Iraq	438,315	169,235	22,219,000
Ireland	70,285	27,135	3,644,000
Israel	21,055	8130	5,652,000
Italy	301,270	116,320	57,510,000
Jamaica	10,990	4245	2,536,000
Japan	377,800	145,870	126,110,000
Jordan	91,880	35,475	4,333,000
Kazakstan	2,717,300	1,049,155	16,544,000
Kenya	580,365	224,080	28,803,000
Kiribati	725	280	82,500
Korea, North	120,540	46,540	22,000,000
Korea, South	99,265	38,325	45,628,000
Kuwait	17,820	6880	1,809,000
Kyrgyzstan	198,500	76,640	4,595,000
Laos	236,800	91,430	5,117,000
Latvia	64,600	24,940	2,472,000
Lebanon	10,400	4015	3,112,000

World nations, areas, and populations

Nation	Area (sq km)	Area (sq miles)	Population*
Lesotho	30,355	11,720	2,008,000
Liberia	111,370	43,000	2,602,000
Libya	1,759,540	679,360	5,648,000
Liechtenstein	160	60	31,500
Lithuania	65,200	25,175	3,707,000
Luxembourg	2585	1000	420,000
Macedonia	25,715	9930	1,984,000
Madagascar	587,040	226,660	14,062,000
Malawi	118,485	45,745	9,609,000
Malaysia	329,760	127,320	21,767,000
Maldives	300	115	267,000
Mali	1,240,190	478,840	9,945,000
Malta	315	120	375,000
Marshall Islands	180	70	60,500
Mauritania	1,025,520	395,955	2,411,000
Mauritius	2040	790	1,143,000

World nations, areas, and populations

Nation	Area (sq km)	Area (sq miles)	Population*
Mexico	1,958,200	756,066	94,275,000
Micronesia, Federated States of	700	270	109,000
Moldova	33,700	13,010	4,362,000
Monaco	0.75	0.3	32,000
Mongolia	1,566,500	604,830	2,370,000
Morocco	446,550	172,415	26,239,000
Mozambique	801,590	309,495	18,165,000
Myanmar	676,580	261,230	46,822,000
Namibia	824,290	318,260	1,727,000
Nauru	20	8	11,000
Nepal	140,795	54,360	21,424,000
Netherlands	41,525	16,035	15,619,000
New Zealand	270,535	104,455	3,653,000
Nicaragua	130,000	50,195	4,632,000
Niger	1,267,000	489,190	9,389,000
Nigeria	923,770	356,670	103,460,000

World nations, areas, and populations

Nation	Area (sq km)	Area (sq miles)	Population*
Norway	386,960	149,405	4,405,000
Oman	212,455	82,030	2,265,000
Pakistan	796,095	307,375	136,183,000
Palau (Belau)	460	175	17,000
Panama	78,200	30,195	2,719,000
Papua New Guinea	462,840	178,705	4,496,000
Paraguay	406,750	157,050	5,089,000
Peru	1,285,215	496,225	24,371,000
Philippines	300,000	115,830	71,539,000
Poland	312,675	120,725	38,802,000
Portugal	92,390	35,670	9,943,000
Qatar	11,000	4245	561,000
Romania	237,500	91,700	22,600,000
Russia	17,075,400	6,592,850	147,976,000
Rwanda	26,340	10,170	7,738,000
St. Kitts-Nevis	260	100	42,000

World nations, areas, and populations

Nation	Area (sq km)	Area (sq miles)	Population*
St. Lucia	620	240	148,000
St. Vincent and the Grenadines	390	150	112,000
Samoa	2830	1095	169,000
San Marino	60	25	25,500
Sao Tomé and Principe	965	370	137,000
Saudi Arabia	2,149,690	830,000	19,072,000
Senegal	196,720	75,955	9,404,000
Seychelles	455	175	77,500
Sierra Leone	71,740	27,700	4,424,000
Singapore	620	240	3,104,000
Slovakia	49,035	18,935	5,404,000
Slovenia	20,295	7835	1,955,000
Solomon Islands	28,895	11,155	411,000
Somalia	637,655	246,200	6,870,000

World nations, areas, and populations

Nation	Area (sq km)	Area (sq miles)	Population*
South Africa	1,221,035	471,445	42,446,000
Spain	504,780	194,895	39,323,000
Sri Lanka	65,610	25,330	18,663,000
Sudan	2,505,815	967,500	32,594,000
Suriname	163,265	63,035	424,000
Swaziland	17,365	6705	1,032,000
Sweden	449,965	173,730	8,863,000
Switzerland	41,295	15,945	7,116,000
Syria	185,180	71,500	15,009,000
Taiwan	35,980	13,890	21,616,000
Tajikistan	143,100	55,250	5,513,000
Tanzania	945,085	364,900	29,461,000
Thailand	513,115	198,115	60,700,000
Togo	56,785	21,925	4,736,000
Tonga	745	290	101,500
Trinidad and Tobago	5130	1980	1,276,000

World nations, areas, and populations

Nation	Area (sq km)	Area (sq miles)	Population*
Tunisia	163,610	63,170	9,218,000
Turkey	770,450	300,950	63,528,000
Turkmenistan	488,100	188,455	4,695,000
Tuvalu	25	10	10,500
Uganda	235,880	91,075	20,605,000
Ukraine	603,700	233,090	50,668,000
United Arab Emirates	83,600	32,280	2,580,000
United Kingdom	244,175	94,275	58,919,000
United States	9,363,565	3,615,290	267,839,000
Uruguay	177,415	68,500	3,185,000
Uzbekistan	447,400	172,740	23,664,000
Vanuatu	12,190	4705	176,500
Vatican City	0.44	0.17	1000
Venezuela	912,050	352,145	22,777,000
Vietnam	331,690	128,065	72,124,000

World nations, areas, and populations

Nation	Area (sq km)	Area (sq miles)	Population*
Yemen	527,970	203,850	16,496,000
Yugoslavia	102,175	39,450	10,632,000
Zambia	752,620	290,585	9,350,000
Zimbabwe	390,755	150,870	11,423,000

* Latest figure or estimate

28. Capital cities and populations

Country	City	Population*
Afghanistan	Kabul	700,000
Albania	Tirane	244,500
Algeria	Algiers	1,722,000
Andorra	Andorra-la-Vella	20,500
Angola	Luanda	2,250,000
Antigua and Barbuda	St John's	21,500
Argentina	Buenos Aires	11,256,000
Armenia	Yerevan	1,202,000
Australia	Canberra	300,000
Austria	Vienna	1,533,500
Azerbaijan	Baku	1,799,500
Bahamas	Nassau	172,000
Bahrain	Manama	140,500
Bangladesh	Dhaka	3,398,000
Barbados	Bridgetown	7,000
Belarus	Minsk	1,613,000
Belgium	Brussels	954,000
Belize	Belmopan	6,000
Benin	Porto-Novo	179,500
Bhutan	Thimphu	30,500

Capital cities and populations

Country	City	Population*
Bolivia	La Paz (administrative)	711,000
Bolivia	Sucre (judicial)	131,000
Bosnia-Hercegovina	Sarajevo	200,000
Botswana	Gaborone	133,500
Brazil	Brasilia	1,601,000
Brunei	Bandar Seri Begawan	46,000
Bulgaria	Sofia	1,221,000
Burkina Faso	Ouagadougou	442,500
Burundi	Bujumbura	235,500
Cambodia	Phnom Penh	920,000
Cameroon	Yaounde	800,000
Canada	Ottawa	314,000
Cape Verde	Praia	62,000
Central African Republic	Bangui	577,000
Chad	N'Djamena	531,000
Chile	Santiago	5,181,000
China	Beijing	10,819,000
Colombia	Bogota	4,921,000
Comoros	Moroni	20,000

Capital cities and populations

Country	City	Population*
Congo, Democratic Republic	Kinshasa	3,804,000
Congo, Republic of	Brazzaville	2,936,000
Costa Rica	San José	319,000
Côte d'Ivoire	Abidjan	1,929,100
Croatia	Zagreb	707,000
Cuba	Havana	2,241,000
Cyprus	Nicosia	186,500
Czech Republic	Prague	1,212,000
Denmark	Copenhagen	467,000
Djibouti	Djibouti	290,000
Dominica	Roseau	16,000
Dominican Republic	Santo Domingo	2,055,000
Ecuador	Quito	1,400,500
Egypt	Cairo	6,663,000
El Salvador	San Salvador	422,500
Equatorial Guinea	Malabo	37,000
Eritrea	Asmara	367,500
Estonia	Tallinn	505,000
Ethiopia	Addis Ababa	2,316,400

Capital cities and populations

Country	City	Population*
Fiji	Suva	71,500
Finland	Helsinki	492,500
France	Paris	2,175,500
Gabon	Libreville	352,000
Gambia	Banjul	44,500
Georgia	Tbilisi	1,267,500
Germany	Berlin	3,446,000
Ghana	Accra	867,450
Greece	Athens	784,150
Grenada	St George's	4,500
Guatemala	Guatemala City	1,167,500
Guinea	Conakry	950,000
Guinea-Bissau	Bissau	125,000
Guyana	Georgetown	185,000
Haiti	Port-au-Prince	1,255,000
Honduras	Tegucigalpa	670,500
Hungary	Budapest	2,000,000
Iceland	Reykjavik	97,500
India	New Delhi	294,000
Indonesia	Jakarta	8,222,500
Iran	Teheran	6,750,000

Capital cities and populations

Country	City	Population*
Iraq	Baghdad	4,648,500
Ireland	Dublin	478,000
Israel	Jerusalem	562,000
Italy	Rome	2,791,500
Jamaica	Kingston	538,500
Japan	Tokyo	8,163,000
Jordan	Amman	965,000
Kazakhstan	Almaty	1,515,300
Kenya	Nairobi	1,346,000
Kiribati	Tarawa	29,000
Korea, North	Pyongyang	2,000,000
Korea, South	Seoul	10,628,000
Kuwait	Kuwait City	44,500
Kyrgyzstan	Bishkek	625,000
Laos	Vientiane	377,500
Latvia	Riga	916,500
Lebanon	Beirut	1,500,000
Lesotho	Maseru	367,000
Liberia	Monrovia	500,000
Libya	Tripoli	991,000

Capital cities and populations

Country	City	Population*
Liechtenstein	Vaduz	5,000
Lithuania	Vilnius	593,000
Luxembourg	Luxembourg	76,000
Macedonia	Skopje	440,500
Madagascar	Antananarivo	802,400
Malawi	Lilongwe	234,000
Malaysia	Kuala Lumpur	145,000
Maldives	Malé	55,000
Mali	Bamako	600,000
Malta	Valletta	102,000
Marshall Islands	Majuro	20,000
Mauritania	Nouakchott	850,000
Mauritius	Port Louis	143,500
Mexico	Mexico City	13,636,000
Micronesia	Palikir	20,000
Moldova	Chisinau	676,000
Mongolia	Ulan Bator	575,000
Morocco	Rabat	1,220,000
Mozambique	Maputo	1,098,000
Myanmar	Rangoon	2,459,000
Namibia	Windhoek	58,500

Capital cities and populations

Country	City	Population*
Nepal	Kathmandu	419,000
Netherlands	Amsterdam	702,450
New Zealand	Wellington	150,500
Nicaragua	Managua	682,500
Niger	Niamey	410,000
Nigeria	Abuja	378,650
Norway	Oslo	458,500
Oman	Muscat	380,000
Pakistan	Islamabad	201,000
Palau (Belau)	Koror	10,500
Panama Fed. States of	Panama City	585,000
Papua New Guinea	Port Moresby	193,500
Paraguay	Asuncion	637,750
Peru	Lima	5,706,000
Philippines	Manila	1,600,000
Poland	Warsaw	1,655,500
Poland	Warsaw	1,655,500
Portugal	Lisbon	678,000
Qatar	Doha	300,000
Romania	Bucharest	2,344,000

Capital cities and populations

Country	City	Population
Russia	Moscow	8,801,000
Rwanda	Kigali	234,500
Samoa	Apia	32,000
San Marino	San Marino	15,500
Sana	Yemen	926,500
Sao Tomé	Sao Tomé	43,500
Saudi Arabia	Riyadh	2,000,000
Senegal	Dakar	1,641,500
Serbia	Belgrade	1,168,500
Seychelles	Victoria	24,000
Sierra Leone	Freetown	505,000
Singapore	Singapore	2,874,000
Slovakia	Bratislava	441,500
Slovenia	Ljubljana	267,000
Solomon Islands	Honiara	35,500
Somalia	Mogadishu	377,000
South Africa (administrative capital)	Pretoria	1,080,000
South Africa (judicial capital)	Bloemfontein	300,500
South Africa (legislative capital)	Cape Town	776,500

Capital cities and populations

Country	City	Population
Spain	Madrid	2,984,500
Sri Lanka	Colombo	615,000
St Kitts-Nevis	Basseterre	12,500
St Lucia	Castries	14,000
St Vincent	Kingstown	26,500
Sudan	Khartoum	924,500
Suriname	Paramaribo	201,000
Swaziland	Mbabane	38,500
Sweden	Stockholm	674,500
Switzerland	Berne	134,500
Syria	Damascus	1,497,000
Taiwan	Taipei	2,718,000
Tajikistan	Dushanbe	602,000
Tanzania	Dodoma	204,000
Thailand	Bangkok	5,876,000
Togo	Lome	450,000
Tonga	Nukualofa	22,000
Trinidad and Tobago	Port-of-Spain	46,000
Tunisia	Tunis	597,000
Turkey	Ankara	2,559,500

Capital cities and populations

Country	City	Population
Turkmenistan	Ashgabat	412,200
Tuvalu	Funafuti	10,000
Uganda	Kampala	773,500
Ukraine	Kiev	2,616,000
United Arab Emirates	Abu Dhabi	928,350
United Kingdom	London	6,379,000
United States	Washington, D.C.	607,000
Uruguay	Montevideo	1,360,500
Uzbekistan	Tashkent	2,094,000
Vanuatu	Port-Vila	19,500
Venezuela	Caracas	1,825,000
Vietnam	Hanoi	925,000
Zambia	Lusaka	982,000
Zimbabwe	Harare	1,184,000

* Latest figures or estimate

29. Largest islands and areas

Island	Ocean where located	Area (sq km)	Area (sq miles)
Greenland	Atlantic	2,175,600	840,000
New Guinea	Pacific	800,000	308,900
Borneo	Pacific	744,100	287,300
Madagascar	Indian	587,100	226,700
Baffin	Arctic	476,100	183,800
Sumatra	Indian	425,000	164,000
Honshu	Pacific	231,000	89,200
Great Britain	Atlantic	218,100	84,200
Victoria	Arctic	217,200	83,900
Ellesmere	Arctic	196,100	75,700
Sulawesi	Indian	189,200	73,100
South Island (New Zealand)	Pacific	149,900	57,900
Java	Indian	126,600	48,900
North Island (New Zealand)	Pacific	114,700	44,300
Cuba	Atlantic	110,900	42,800

30. Largest freshwater lakes and areas

Lake	Location (continent)	Area (sq km)	(sq miles)
Superior	North America	82,070	31,690
Victoria	Africa	69,470	26,820
Huron	North America	59,550	22,990
Michigan	North America	57,740	22,290
Tanganyika	Africa	32,880	12,700
Baikal	Asia	31,500	12,160
Great Bear	North America	31,320	12,090
Malawi/Nyasa	Africa	28,900	11,100
Great Slave	North America	28,570	11,030
Lake Erie	North America	25,670	9,910

Note: The Caspian Sea is a saltwater lake.

31. Largest deserts and areas

Desert	Continent where located	Area (sq km)	Area (sq miles)
Sahara	Africa	9,000,000	5,592,500
Rub al-Khali (Arabian)	Asia	1,300,000	502,000
Gobi	Asia	1,036,000	400,000
Patagonian	South America	673,000	250,000
Kalahari	Africa	520,800	201,000
Great Sandy	Australasia	415,500	160,000
Taklimakan	Asia	327,600	126,300
Chihuahuan	North America	362,600	140,000
Great Victoria	Australasia	338,500	131,000
Kyzyl Kum	Asia	259,000	100,000

32. Largest oceans and seas

Name	Area		Average depth	
	(sq km)	(sq miles)	(meters)	(feet)
Pacific Ocean	166,240,000	64,200,000	3950	12,900
Atlantic Ocean	86,560,000	33,420,000	3600	11,700
Indian Ocean	73,430,000	28,350,000	3850	12,600
Arctic Ocean	13,220,000	5,110,000	1050	3400
South China Sea	2,980,000	1,150,000	1450	4800
Caribbean Sea	2,750,000	1,050,000	2550	8450
Mediterranean Sea	2,510,000	970,000	1500	4900
Bering Sea	2,260,000	870,000	1500	4900
Sea of Okhotsk	1,580,000	610,000	1000	3300
Gulf of Mexico	1,550,000	600,000	1600	5300

Note: The Caspian Sea and the Aral Sea are lakes

33. Highest mountains and heights

Mountain	Continent where located	Height (meters)	Height (feet)
Everest	Asia (China/Nepal)	8848	29,029
K2	Asia (China/Kashmir)	8611	28,251
Kangchenjunga	Asia (India/Nepal)	8598	28,209
Lhotse	Asia (China/Nepal)	8510	27,920
Makalu I	Asia (China/Nepal)	8470	27,790
Dhaulagiri I	Asia (Nepal)	8172	26,810
Manaslu I	Asia (Nepal)	8155	26,755
Cho Oyu	Asia (Nepal)	8153	26,750
Nanga Parbat	Asia (Kashmir)	8125	26,657
Annapurna I	Asia (Nepal)	8078	26,503

34. Longest rivers and lengths

River	Continent where located	Length (kilometers)	(miles)
Nile	Africa	6670	4145
Amazon	South America	6448	4007
Yangtze (Chang Jiang)	Asia	6300	3915
Mississippi–Missouri	North America	6020	3741
Yenisey–Angara	Asia	5540	3442
Yellow (Huang He)	Asia	5464	3395
Ob–Irtysh	Asia	5410	3362
Amur–Shilka	Asia	4416	2744
Congo	Africa	4374	2718
Mekong	Asia	4350	2703
Mackenzie–Peace -Finlay	North America	4241	2635
Niger	Africa	4100	2548
Paraná	South America	3943	2450
Murray–Darling	Australasia	3751	2331
Volga	Asia	3685	2290

35. Highest Waterfalls

Name	Location	Source	Height	
			Ft	Meters
Angel	Venezuela	Rio Caroni	3,212	979
Tugela	South Africa	Tugela River	3,110	947
Utigord	Norway	Jostedal Glacier	2,625	800
Mongefoseen	Norway	Mongebekk	2,540	774
Yosemite	United States	Yosemite Creek	2,425	739
Mardalsfossen	Norway	Mardals River	2,154	656
Tyssestrengane	Norway	Tysso River	2,123	647
Cuquenan	Venezuela	Cuquenan River	2,000	610
Sutherland	New Zeland	Arthur River	1,904	580
Takakkaw	Canada	Daly Glacier	1,650	502

36. Highest and Lowest Annual Precipitation

Place	Higest Annual Average (in)
Lloro, Colombia	524
Mawsynram, India	467
Mt. Waialeale, Kauai	460
Debundscha, Cameroon	405
Quibdo, Colombia	350
Bellenden Ker, Queensland	340
Henderson Lake, British Columbia	256

LOWEST

Place	Lowest Annual Average (in)
Arica, Chile	0.03
Hadi Halfa, Sudan	0.10
Amundsen-Scott South Pole Station	0.8
Batagues, Mexico	1.3
Aden, Yemen	1.8
Mulka, South Australia	4.0
Astrakhan, Russia	6.4

37. Elements, atomic number, relative atomic mass (r.a.m.)

Name	Symbol	At. no.	R.a.m.
actinium	Ac	89	26.982
aluminum	Al	13	26.9815
americium	Am	95	(243)
antimony	Sb	51	121.75
argon	Ar	18	39.948
arsenic	As	33	74.9216
astatine	At	85	(210)
barium	Ba	56	137.34
berkelium	Bk	97	(247)
beryllium	Be	4	9.0122
bismuth	Bi	83	208.9806
bohrium	Bh	107	(262)
boron	B	5	10.81
bromine	Br	35	79.904
cadmium	Cd	48	112.40
calcium	Ca	20	40.08
californium	Cf	98	(251)
carbon	C	6	12.001
cerium	Ce	58	140.12
cesium	Cs	55	132.9055
chlorine	CI	17	35.453
chromium	Cr	24	51.996
cobalt	Co	27	58.9332

Elements, atomic number, relative atomic mass (r.a.m.)

Name	Symbol	At. no.	R.a.m.
copper	Cu	29	63.546
curium	Cm	96	(247)
dubnium	Db	105	(262)
dysprosium	Dy	66	162.50
einsteinium	Es	99	(252)
erbium	Er	68	167.26
europium	Eu	63	151.96
fermium	Fm	100	(257)
fluorine	F	9	18.9984
francium	Fr	87	(223)
gadolinium	Gd	64	157.25
gallium	Ga	31	69.72
germanium	Ge	32	72.59
gold	Au	79	196.9665
hafnium	Hf	72	178.49
hassium	Hs	108	(265)
helium	He	2	4.0026
holmium	Ho	67	164.9303
hydrogen	H	1	1.0080
indium	In	49	114.82
iodine	I	53	126.904
iridium	Ir	77	192.22
iron	Fe	26	55.847

Elements, atomic number, relative atomic mass (r.a.m.)

Name	Symbol	At. no.	R.a.m.
krypton	Kr	36	83.80
lanthanum	La	57	138.9055
lawrencium	Lr	103	(262)
lead	Pb	82	207.19
lithium	Li	3	6.941
lutetium	Lu	71	174.97
magnesium	Mg	12	24.305
manganese	Mn	25	54.9380
meitnerium	Mt	109	(266)
mendelevium	Md	101	(258)
mercury	Hg	80	200.59
molybdenum	Mo	42	95.94
neodymium	Nd	60	144.24
neon	Ne	10	20.179
neptunium	Np	93	(237)
nickel	Ni	28	58.71
niobium	Nb	41	92.9064
nitrogen	N	7	14.0067
nobelium	No	102	(259)
osmium	Os	76	190.2
oxygen	O	8	15.9994
palladium	Pd	46	106.4
phosphorus	P	15	30.9738

Elements, atomic number, relative atomic mass (r.a.m.)

Name	Symbol	At. no.	R.a.m.
platinum	Pt	78	195.09
plutonium	Pu	94	(244)
polonium	Po	84	(209)
potassium	K	19	39.102
praseodymium	Pr	59	140.9077
promethium	Pm	61	(145)
protactinium	Pa	91	231.0359
radium	Ra	88	226.0254
radon	Rn	86	(222)
rhenium	Re	75	186.20
rhodium	Rh	45	102.9055
rubidium	Rb	37	85.4678
ruthenium	Ru	44	101.07
rutherfordium	Rf	104	(261)
samarium	Sm	62	150.35
scandium	Sc	21	44.9559
seaborgium	Sg	106	(263)
selenium	Se	34	78.96
silicon	Si	14	28.086
silver	Ag	47	107.868
sodium	Na	11	22.9898
strontium	Sr	38	87.62
sulfur	S	16	32.06

Elements, atomic number, relative atomic mass (r.a.m.)

Name	Symbol	At. no.	R.a.m.
tantalum	Ta	73	180.9479
technetium	Tc	43	(99)
tellurium	Te	52	127.60
terbium	Tb	65	158.9254
thallium	Tl	81	204.39
thorium	Th	90	232.0381
thulium	Tm	69	168.9342
tin	Sn	50	118.69
titanium	Ti	22	47.90
tungsten	W	74	183.85
uranium	U	92	238.029
vanadium	V	23	50.9414
xenon	Xe	54	131.30
ytterbium	Yb	70	173.04
yttrium	Y	39	88.9059
zinc	Zn	30	65.38
zirconium	Zr	40	91.22

Relative atomic masses in brackets are those of the longest-lived isotopes of radioactive elements.

38. Periodic table

1 H								
3 Li	4 Be							
11 Na	12 Mg							
19 K	20 Ca	21 Sc	22 Ti	23 V	24 Cr	25 Mn	26 Fe	27 Co
37 Rb	38 Sr	39 Y	40 Zr	41 Nb	42 Mo	43 Tc	44 Ru	45 Rh
55 Cs	56 Ba	57 La	72 Hf	73 Ta	74 W	75 Re	76 Os	77 Ir
87 Fr	88 Ra	89 Ac	104 Rf	105 Db	106 Sg	107 Bh	108 Hs	109 Mt

lanthanides:	58 Ce	59 Pr	60 Nd	61 Pm	62 Sm
actinides:	90 Th	91 Pa	92 U	93 Np	94 Pu

								2 He
			5 B	6 C	7 N	8 O	9 F	10 Ne
			13 Al	14 Si	15 P	16 S	17 Cl	18 Ar
28 Ni	29 Cu	30 Zn	31 Ga	32 Ge	33 As	34 Se	35 Br	36 Kr
46 Pd	47 Ag	48 Cd	49 In	50 Sn	51 Sb	52 Te	53 I	54 Xe
78 Pt	79 Au	80 Hg	81 Ti	82 Pb	83 Bi	84 Po	85 At	86 Rn

63 Eu	64 Gd	65 Tb	66 Dy	67 Ho	68 Er	69 Tm	70 Yb	71 Lu
95 Am	96 Cm	97 Bk	98 Cf	99 Es	100 Fm	101 Md	102 No	103 Lr

39. Decibel scale

Decibels (dB)	Loudness	Examples
200	deafening	Large-caliber naval gun
180		Military jet plane nearby
170		Space Shuttle at take-off
150		Rock band flat out
140		Commercial jet at take-off
130		Threshold of pain
120		Thunder overhead
110		Nearby jackhammer
100	very loud	Chainsaw
90		Military band
80	loud	Train passing, police siren
70		Alarm clock, busy street
60	moderately loud	Close-up conversation
50		Children's party
40	faint	Residential neighborhood
30		Quiet conversation
20	very faint	Watch ticking, whisper
10		Soundproof room
0		Threshold of hearing

40. Basic equations in physics

Acceleration a

$a = F/m$

where F = force, m = mass

$a = (v - u)/t$

where v = final velocity, u = initial velocity, t = time

Capacitance C

$C = Q/V$

where Q = charge, V = voltage

Charge Q

$Q = It$

where I = current, t = time

for a stationary charge, $Q = F/E$

where F = force, E = electrical field strength

for a capacitor, $Q = CV$

where C = capacitance, V = voltage

Current I

$I = V/R$

where V = voltage, R = resistance

$I = P/V$

where P = power, V = voltage

$I = Q/t$

where Q = charge, t = time

Basic equations in physics

Density d

$d = m/V$

where m = mass, V = volume

Displacement s

$s = vt$

where v = velocity, t = time

$s = ut + \frac{1}{2}at^2$

where u = initial velocity, a = acceleration, t = time

$s = (v^2 - u^2)/2a$

where v = final velocity, u = initial velocity, a = acceleration

Energy W

$W = Fs$

where F = force, s = displacement

$W = mgh$

where m = mass, g = acceleration of free fall, h = height

$W = \frac{1}{2}mv^2$

where m = mass, v = velocity

Focal distance f

for a lens, $1/f = 1/v + 1/u$

where v = image distance, u = object distance

for a curved mirror, $f = r/2$

where r = radius of curvature

Basic equations in physics

Force F
$F = ma$
where m = mass, a = acceleration

$F = W/s$
where W = work (energy), s = displacement

$F = P/v$
where P = power, v = velocity

Mass m
$m = F/a$
where F = force, a = acceleration

$m = dV$
where d = density, V = volume

$m = W/g$
where W = weight, g = acceleration of free fall

Moment of a force
moment = Fs
where F = force, s = displacement

Momentum
momentum = mv
where m = mass, v = velocity

Power (mechanical) P
$P = Fv$
where F = force, v = velocity

Basic equations in physics

$P = W/t$
where W = work (energy), t = time

Power (electrical) P

$P = VI$
where V = voltage, I = current

$P = I^2 R$
where I = current, R = resistance

$P = V^2/R$
where V = voltage, R = resistance

$P = W/t$
where W = electrical energy, t = time

Power (of a lens or mirror) P

$P = 1/f$
where f = focal distance

Pressure p

$p = F/A$
where F = force, A = area

for a liquid, $p = hdg$
where h = height (depth), d = density of fluid, g = acceleration of free fall

for an ideal gas, $p = kT/V$
where k = Boltzmann's constant, T = absolute temperature, V = volume

Basic equations in physics

Resistance R

$R = V/I$

where V = voltage, I = current

Speed S

$S = l/t$

where l = distance, t = time

Velocity v

$v = s/t$

where s = displacement, t = time

$v = u + at$

where u = initial velocity, a = acceleration, t = time

$v^2 = u^2 + 2as$

where u = initial velocity, a = acceleration, s = displacement

Voltage V

$V = IR$

where I = current, R = resistance

for a capacitor, $V = Q/C$

where Q = charge, C = capacitance

Weight W

$W = mg$

where m = mass, g = acceleration of free fall

Work W

$W = Fs$

where F = force, s = displacement

41. Colors of the spectrum

Visible spectrum:

Color	Wavelength (nm)
red	780–660
orange	660–600
yellow	550–600
green	475–550
blue	440–475
indigo	400–440
violet	380–400

Electromagnetic spectrum:

Radiation	Wavelength	Frequency (Hz)
radio waves	10^5-10^2 cm	10^5-10^8
microwaves	10^2-10^{-2} cm	10^8-10^{10}
infrared	10^{-1}-7.8×10^{-5} cm	1.5×10^{11}-1.8×10^{14}
visible light	0.78 -0.38 µm	1.8×10^{14}-1.95×10^{14}
ultraviolet	0.38-0.03 µm	1.95×10^{14}-1.7×10^{16}
X-rays	1.0-0.001 nm	1.7×10^{16}-10^{20}
gamma rays	0.001-0.000001 nm	10^{20}-10^{22}

42. Properties of some metals

Metal	Melting point (°C)	Boiling point (°C)	Relative density
aluminum	661	2467	2.68
barium	725	1637	3.60
beryllium	1278	2970	1.93
bismuth	271	1560	9.70
cadmium	321	756	8.65
calcium	839	1484	1.58
cerium	798	3426	6.70
chromium	1857	2672	7.14
cobalt	1495	2870	8.90
copper	1083	2567	9.00
gold	1064	2807	19.30
iridium	2410	4130	22.40
iron	1535	2750	7.86
lead	333	1740	11.35
magnesium	649	1090	11.74
manganese	1244	1962	7.39

Properties of some metals

Metal	Melting point (°C)	Boiling point (°C)	Relative density
mercury	-39	357	13.60
molybdenum	2617	4612	10.20
nickel	1453	2732	8.90
osmium	3045	5027	22.48
palladium	1554	3140	11.40
platinum	1772	3800	21.45
plutonium	641	3330	19.80
silver	962	2212	10.50
tin	232	2270	7.30
titanium	1660	3287	4.50
tungsten	3410	5700	19.10
uranium	1132	3754	18.68
vanadium	1890	3377	5.50
zinc	420	907	7.12

43. Classes of chemical compounds

Type of compound	Description	Example
acid	compound that releases hydrogen ions (H+) in solution; reacts with a base to form a salt and water; turns litmus red	hydrochloric acid HCl
acidic oxide	oxide of a nonmetal that reacts with water to form an acid and with a base to form a salt and water	carbon dioxide CO_2
alkali	compound that is a soluble base or a solution of a base; liberates hydroxyl (OH−) ions in solution; reacts with an acid to form a salt	sodium hydroxide $NaOH$
alum	double sulfate salt of a monovalent metal and a trivalent metal	potassium alum $K_2SO_4.Al_2(SO_4)_3$ $24H_2O$
amphoteric compound	compound that reacts with either an acid or an alkali to form a salt	aluminum oxide Al_2O_3
anhydride	compound formed by chemically removing water from another compound	sulfur trioxide SO_3
base	compound that reacts with an acid to form a salt; turns litmus blue	calcium oxide CaO

Classes of chemical compounds

Type of compound	Description	Example
basic oxide	metal oxide that reacts with water to form a base and with an acid to form a salt and water	sodium oxide Na_2O
basic salt	type of salt that contains hydroxide (OH–) ions	basic lead carbonate $2PbCO_3.Pb(OH)_2$
bromide	compound of bromine and another element; salt of hydrobromic acid	potassium bromide KBr
carbonate	salt of carbonic acid	calcium carbonate $CaCO_3$
chloride	compound of chlorine and another element; salt of hydrochloric acid	sodium chloride $NaCl$
hydroxide	compound of a metal that contains one or more hydroxide (OH-) ions or groups	calcium hydroxide $Ca(OH)_2$
inorganic compound	any compound other than those of carbon (but including carbon oxides, carbonates, etc.)	iron sulfide FeS
iodide	compound of iodine and another element; salt of hydroiodic acid	potassium iodide KI

Classes of chemical compounds

Type of compound	Description	Example
neutral oxide	oxide that does not react with water; it is neither acidic nor basic	carbon monoxide CO
nitrate	salt of nitric acid	silver nitrate $AgNO_3$
organic compound	any compound of carbon (except carbon oxides, carbonates, etc.)	methane CH_4
oxide	compound of oxygen and another element	sulfur dioxide SO_2
phosphate	salt of phosphoric acid	sodium phosphate Na_3PO_4
salt	compound formed by the interaction of an acid and a base; soluble salts form ions in solution	ammonium chloride NH_4Cl
sulfate	salt of sulfuric acid	zinc sulfate $ZnSO_4$
sulfide	compound of sulfur and another element	lead sulfide PbS

44. Densities of some gases

Gas	Density (kg/m³)
air	1.30
argon	1.80
butane	0.58
carbon dioxide	1.98
chlorine	3.20
helium	0.18
hydrogen	0.09
isobutane	2.60
methane	0.72
neon	0.90
nitrogen	1.25
oxygen	1.43
propane	2.02
radon	9.70
xenon	5.90

45. Solar system

Planets:

Name	Distance from Sun (million km)			Orbital period around Sun (in Earth days/years)
	max.	min.	mean	
Mercury	69.7	45.9	57.9	87.97 days
Venus	109.0	107.4	108.2	224.7 days
Earth	152	147	150	365.26 days
Mars	249	207	228	686.9 days
Jupiter	816	741	778	11.86 years
Saturn	1507	1347	1427	29.46 years
Uranus	3004	2735	2871	84.01 years
Neptune	4537	4456	4497	164.8 years
Pluto	7375	4425	5914	247.7 years

Major planetary satellites*:

Planet	Satellite(s)	Diameter (km)	Rotational period (days)	Average distance from parent planet (km)
Earth	Moon	3476	27.32	384,400
Mars	Deimos	15 x 12	1.26	23,450
	Phobos	26 x 16	0.32	9380

Solar system

Major planetary satellites*:

Planet	Satellite(s)	Diameter (km)	Rotational period (days)	Average distance from parent planet (km)
Jupiter	Amalthea	270 x 160	0.50	181,300
	Callisto	4800	16.69	1,883,000
	Elara	75	259.7	11,737,000
	Europa	3140	3.55	671,000
	Ganymede	5260	7.15	1,070,000
	Himalia	185	250.6	11,480,000
	Io	3640	1.77	422,000
Saturn	Dione	1120	2.74	377,400
	Enceladus	250	1.37	238,000
	Hyperion	370 x 280	21.3	1,481,000
	Iapetus	1435	79.3	3,561,000
	Mimas	400	0.94	185,500
	Phoebe	230 x 220	550.5	12,952,000
	Rhea	1530	4.52	527,000
	Tethys	1060	1.89	295,000
	Titan	5150	15.9	1,222,000
Uranus	Ariel	1160	2.52	191,250
	Oberon	1520	13.5	582,500
	Titania	1580	8.71	435,850
	Umbriel	1170	4.14	265,950
Neptune	Nereid	340	360.1	5,513,500
	Triton	2705	5.88	354,750
Pluto	Charon	1190	6.39	19,650

* Mercury and Venus have no natural satellites

Solar system

Major asteroids:

Name	Year found	Diameter (km)	Distance from Sun (million km)	Orbital period around Sun (in Earth years)
Ceres	1801	935	415.5	4.60
Pallas	1802	525	415.5	4.60
Juno	1804	265	399.8	4.36
Vesta	1807	500	354.0	3.63
Astrea	1845	125	387.0	4.14
Hebe	1847	190	363.8	3.78
Iris	1847	205	358.5	3.69
Flora	1847	160	330.8	3.27
Metis	1848	190	357.8	3.68
Hygeia	1849	430	469.5	5.59

Major comets:

Name	Year found	Closest distance to Sun (million km)	Orbital period around Sun (in Earth years)
Biela	1772	129	6.6
Encke	178	14.8	3.3
Hale-Bopp	1995		1000
Halley	240BC	88.3	76
Ikeya-Seki	1965	1.2	880
Kohoutek	1973	21.0	70,000
Swift-Tuttle	1862	144	120
Tempel-Tuttle	1366		33
West	1975	29.2	500,000
Whipple	1951	460	8.5

46. Planetary data

Name	Equatorial diameter (km)	Mass (Earth = 1)	Volume (Earth = 1)	Rotation period	Gravity (m/sec²)
Mercury	4878	0.055	0.056	58.65 days	3.70
Venus	12,104	0.815	0.86	243.01 days	8.87
Earth	12,756	1	1	23.93 hours	9.78
Mars	6795	0.107	0.15	24.62 hours	3.72
Jupiter	142,985	318	1320	9.84 hours	22.88
Saturn	120,536	95	744	10.23 hours	9.05
Uranus	51,118	15	67	17.23 hours	7.77
Neptune	50,538	17	57	19.12 hours	11.00
Pluto	2320	0.003	0.01	6.39 days	0.40

Name	Escape velocity (km/sec)	Mean density (gm/cm³)	Mean surface temperature (°C)	(°F)	Inclination of orbit (degrees)
Mercury	4.25	5.43	+480	+896	7.00
Venus	10.36	5.25	+167	+333	3.39
Earth	11.18	5.52	+22	+72	0.00
Mars	5.12	3.95	-23	-9	1.85
Jupiter	59.56	1.33	-150	-238	1.31
Saturn	35.49	0.69	-180	-292	2.49
Uranus	21.30	1.29	-210	-346	0.77
Neptune	23.50	1.64	-220	-364	1.77
Pluto	1.22	2.13	-230	-382	11.15

47. Most common elements of the Sun and Moon

Most Common Elements on the Sun

Element	Abundance (% of total mass)
Hydrogen	71.0
Helium	27.1
Oxygen	.97
Carbon	.40
Nitrogen	.096
Silicon	.099
Magnesium	.076
Neon	.058
Iron	.014
Sulfur	.040

Most Common Elements on the Moon

(This list is based on the chemical analysis of rock samples brought back to Earth):

Oxygen	Silicon
Iron	Calcium
Titanium	Aluminum
Magnesium	Sodium
Potassium	Chromium

48. Star distances (some of the brightest stars)

Common name	Astronomical name	Distance (light-years)	Apparent magnitude (brightness)*
Achernar	Alpha Eridani	144	0.5
Acrux	Alpha Crucis	510	0.8
Adhara	Epsilon Canis Majoris	431	1.5
Aldebaran	Alpha Tauri	65	0.9
Altair	Alpha Aquilae	17	0.8
Antares	Alpha Scorpii	604	1.0
Arcturus	Alpha Boötes	36	0.0
Bellatrix	Gamma Orionis	243	1.6
Betelgeuse	Alpha Orionis	427	0.5
Canopus	Alpha Carinae	313	-0.7
Capella	Alpha Aurigae	42	0.1
Castor	Alpha Geminorum	52	1.6
Deneb	Alpha Cygnii	3230	1.3
Formalhaut	Alpha Piscis Austrini	25	1.2
Hadar	Beta Centauri	525	0.6
Mimosa	Beta Crucis	352	1.3
Pollux	Beta Geminorum	34	1.1
Procyon	Alpha Canoris Minoris	11	0.4
Regulus	Alpha Leonis	77	1.4
Rigel	Beta Orionis	773	0.1
Rigel Kent.	Alpha Centaurus	4.3	-0.27
Sirius	Alpha Canis Majoris	8.6	-1.5
Spica	Alpha Virginis	262	1.0
Vega	Alpha Lyrae	25	0.0

* In this list, the brightest is -1.5 and the dimmest is 1.6. The Sun, the brightest star of all as seen from Earth, has an apparent magnitude of -27.

49. Classification of living things

The major levels of classification (called taxonomic groups) are as follows:

	Example	*Example*
Kingdom	Animalia	Plantae
Phylum (for animals) or Division (for plants)	Chordata	Magnoliophyta
Class	Mammalia	Magnoliopsida
Order	Primates	Fagales
Family	Hominidae	Betulaceae
Genus	Homo	Betula
Species	sapiens	pendula
	= human	= silver birch

However, biologists often additionally use various sublevels, and some of these have a characteristic word-ending, as follows on the next page.

Classification of living things

Animals	Suffix	Plants	Suffix
Kingdom		Kingdom	
Subkingdom			
Phylum		Division	-phyta
Subphylum		Subdivision	-phytina
Superclass			
Class		Class	-opsida
Subclass		Subclass	-idae
Infraclass			
Cohort			
Superorder			
Order		Order	-ales
Suborder		Suborder	-ineae
Superfamily	-oidea		
Family	-idae	Family	-aceae
Subfamily	-inae	Subfamily	-oideae
Tribe	-ini	Tribe	-eae
		Subtribe	-inae
Genus		Genus	
Subgenus		Subgenus	
Species		Species	
Subspecies		Subspecies	
		Variety	

50. The five kingdoms (of living things)

Kingdom	Description	Approx. no. of species
Monera	Bacteria and cyanobacteria (photosynthetic blue-green algae)	10,000
Protoctista	Algae, protozoa, and slime molds	100,000
Fungi	Nonphotosynthetic multinucleated organisms	100,000
Plantae	Plants (photosynthetic)	250,000
Animalia	Animals	1,000,000

51. Composition of the human body

Element	Proportion by weight (%, or parts per million = ppm)
oxygen	61%
carbon	23%
hydrogen	10%
nitrogen	2.6%
calcium	1.4%
phosphorus	1.1% (= 11,000 ppm)
sulfur	2000 ppm
potassium	2000 ppm
sodium	1400 ppm
chlorine	1200 ppm
magnesium	270 ppm
silicon	260 ppm
iron	60 ppm
fluorine	37 ppm
zinc	33 ppm
copper	1 ppm

52. Largest organs and longest bones in the human body

Largest Organs in the Human Body

Skin

Liver

Brain

Lungs

Heart

Kidneys

Spleen

Pancreas

Thyroid

Longest Bones in the Human Body

Bone	Avg Length (inches)
Femur (thighbone)	19.88"
Tibia (shinbone)	16.94"
Fibula (outer lower leg)	15.94"
Humerus (upper arm)	14.35"
Ulna (inner lower arm)	11.10"
Radius (outer lower arm)	10.4"
Seventh rib	9.45"
Eighth rib	9.06"

53. Gestation period in some animals

Animal	Pregnancy (days)	Animal	Pregnancy (days)
beaver	122	guinea pig	68
brown bear	240	hog	112–115
buffalo	270	horse	330–342
camel	210	kangaroo	42
cat	57–65	lion	110–115
chimpanzee	230–250	moose	240–250
cow	279–292	mouse	18
deer	200	rabbit	30–35
dog	60–63	rat	23–25
donkey	365	rhinoceros	450
elephant	650–660	sheep	145–150
fox	52	tiger	105–115
giraffe	420–450	whale	360–400
goat	145–155	zebra	365
gorilla	255		

54. Animal data

Heaviest Land Animals*

Mammal	Approx. Weight
African elephant	14,000 lbs. (7,000 kg)
White rhinoceros	8,000 lbs. (3,600 kg)
Hippopotamus	5,500 lbs. (2,500 kg)
Giraffe	3,500 lbs. (1,600 kg)
American bison	2,200 lbs. (1,000 kg)
Dromedary camel (Arabian)	1,500 lbs. (690 kg)

*(Excludes domesticated cattle and horses)

Fastest Land Animals

Mammal	Approx. Speed
Cheetah	65 mph
Wildebeest	61 mph
Lion	50 mph
Elk	45 mph
Cape hunting dog	45 mph
Coyote	43 mph

Heaviest Marine Animals

Mammal	Weight (in tons)
Blue whale	150
Fin whale	50
Right whale	44
Sperm whale	40
Gray whale	36

55. Largest libraries and best-selling books

Largest Libraries in the World

Library	Location	Founded	Approx. # of Books in millions
Library of Congress	Washington, D.C.	1800	25
National Library of China	Beijing	1909	20
National Library of Canada	Ottawa	1953	16
Deutsche Bibliothek	Frankfurt	1947	16
British Library	London	1753	15
Harvard University Library	Cambridge, MA	1638	14
Vernadsky Library	Kiev, Ukraine	1919	13
Russian State Library	Moscow	1862	12
Bibliotheque Nationale de Paris	Paris	1400	11
New York Public Library	New York	1895	10.5

Best-Selling Books of All Time

Book/Author	First Published	Approx. Sales *
The Bible	c. 1450	Over 6 billion
Quotations from the Works of Chairman Mao Tse-Tung	1966	1 billion
American Spelling Book by Noah Webster	1783	100 million
The Guinness Bk. of World Records	1955	90 million
The World Almanac	1868	75 million

* Aggregate sales of various editions

56. Key Inventions

Year	Invention	Inventor(s)	Inventor's nationality
1250	magnifying glass	Roger Bacon	English
1442	printing press	Johann Gutenberg	German
1480	astrolabe	Martin Behaim	German
1505	spring-driven watch	Peter Henlein	German
1550	glass lenses	Girolamo Cardand	Italian
1573	ship's log	Humphray Cole	English
1589	flush toilet	John Harington	English
1598	knitting machine	William Lee	English
1590	compound microscope	Janssen brothers	Dutch
1592	air-filled thermometer	Galileo Galilei	Italian
1600	surveyor's chain	Edmund Gunter	English
1608	telescope	Hans Lippershey	Dutch
1622	slide rule	William Oughtred	English
1631	Vernier gauge	Pierre Vernier	French
1638	micrometer	William Gascoigne	English
1641	adding machine	Blaise Pascal	French
1643	mercury barometer	Evangelista Torricelli	Italian
1650	air pump	Otto von Guericke	German
1656	pendulum clock	Christiaan Huygens	Dutch
1658	watch hairspring	Robert Hooke	English
1666	spirit level	Jean de Thévenot	French
1667	anemometer	Robert Hooke	English
1672	reflecting telescope	Isaac Newton	English
1675	hair-spring watch	Thomas Tompion	English
1675	simple microscope	Anton van Leeuwenhoek	Dutch
1680	pressure cooker	Denis Papin	French
1687	hygrometer	Guillaume Amontons	French

Key Inventions

Year	Invention	Inventor(s)	Inventor's nationality
1698	steam pump	Thomas Savery	British
1701	mechanical seed drill	Jethro Tull	English
1703	vacuum pump	Francis Hawksbee	English
1714	mercury thermometer	Gabriel Fahrenheit	German
1716	diving bell	Edmond Halley	British
1718	flint-lock machine gun	James Puckle	British
1725	stereotype printing	William Ged	Scottish
1728	dental drill	Pierre Fauchard	French
1733	flying shuttle	John Kay	British
1735	chronometer	John Harrison	British
1741	centigrade scale	Anders Celsius	Swedish
1742	steel galvanizing	Paul Malouin	French
1752	lightning conductor	Benjamin Franklin	American
1757	mirror sextant	John Campbell	British
1765	steam engine	James Watt	Scottish
1766	electrometer	Horace de Saussure	Swiss
1768	spinning frame	Richard Arkwright	British
1768	spinning jenny	James Hargreaves	British
1768	threshing machine	Andrew Maikle	Scottish
1769	steam carriage	Nicolas Cugnot	French
1775	horse-drawn tram	John Outram	British
1776	stopwatch	Jean-Moyse Ponzait	Swiss
1776	submarine	David Bushnell	American
1779	spinning mule	Samuel Crompton	British
1782	pyrometer	Josiah Wedgwood	British
1783	hot-air balloon	Montgolfier brothers	French
1783	hydrogen balloon	Jacques Charles	French

Key Inventions

Year	Invention	Inventor(s)	Inventor's nationality
1784	bifocal glasses	Benjamin Franklin	American
1784	unpickable lock	Joseph Bramah	British
1785	steam loom	Edmund Cartwright	British
1787	theodolite	Jesse Ramsden	British
1788	steam paddleboat	Patrick Miller and William Symington	Scottish
1789	guillotine	Joseph Guillotin	French
1789	steam road vehicle	Oliver Evans	American
1790	dentist's chair	Josiah Flagg	American
1790	optical telegraph	Chappe brothers	French
1791	multitube boiler	Nathan Read	American
1792	gas lighting	William Murdock	Scottish
1793	cotton gin	Eli Whitney	American
1795	graphite pencil	Nicolas Conté	French
1795	hydraulic press	Joseph Bramah	British
1797	parachute	André Garnerin	French
1798	lithographic printing	Alloys Senefelder	German
1800	electric battery	Alessandro Volta	Italian
1801	automatic loom	Joseph Jacquard	French
1802	storage battery	Johann Ritter	German
1803	case shot	Henry Shrapnel	British
1804	model glider	George Cayley	British
1804	steam dredger	Oliver Evans	American
1804	steam locomotive	Richard Trevithick	British
1805	percussion cap	Alexander Forsyth	Scottish
1805	solid-fueled rocket	William Congreve	British
1806	carbon paper	Ralph Wedgewood	British

Key Inventions

Year	Invention	Inventor(s)	Inventor's nationality
1807	paddle steamer	Robert Fulton	American
1807	paper-making machine	Fourdrinier brothers	French-British
1808	arc lamp	Humphry Davy	British
1808	lace-making machine	John Heathcoat	British
1810	food canning	Nicholas Appert	French
1810	steam printing press	Friedrich König	German
1812	camera lucida	William Wollaston	British
1813	soda siphon	Charles Plinth	British
1815	paved roads	John McAdam	Scottish
1815	tuneling shield	Marc Brunel	French-British
1816	fire extinguisher	George Manby	British
1816	kaleidoscope	David Brewster	Scottish
1816	metronome	Johann Mäelzel	German
1816	miner's safety lamp	Humphry Davy	British
1816	Stirling engine	Robert Stirling	Scottish
1817	stethoscope	René Laënnec	French
1819	diving suit	Augustus Siebe	German
1819	patent leather	Seth Boyden	American
1820	hygrometer	John Daniell	British
1820	needle galvanometer	Johann Schweigger	German
1823	electromagnet	William Sturgeon	British
1823	waterproof cloth	Charles Mackintosh	Scottish
1824	Portland cement	Joseph Aspidin	British
1825	caterpillar tractor	George Cayley	British
1826	photography (on metal)	Joseph Niépce	French
1827	friction match	John Walker	British

Key Inventions

Year	Invention	Inventor(s)	Inventor's nationality
1827	magnetometer	Johann Poggendorf	German
1827	mechanical reaper	Patrick Bell	Scottish
1827	water turbine	Claude Burdin	French
1828	blast furnace	James Neilson	Scottish
1829	electric motor	Joseph Henry	American
1830	electric telegraph	Samuel Morse	American
1830	sewing machine	Barthélemy Thimonnier	French
1830	thermostat	Andrew Ure	Scottish
1831	dynamo	Michael Faraday	British
1831	electric bell	Joseph Henry	American
1831	platform scales	Thaddeus Fairbanks	American
1831	steam bus	Walter Hancock	British
1832	mechanical computer	Charles Babbage	British
1832	simple screw propeller	Pierre Sauvage	French
1833	reaping machine	Obed Hussey	American
1834	reaper and binder	Cyrus McCormick	American
1834	safety cab	Joseph Hansom	British
1834	shorthand writing	Isaac Pitman	British
1835	electric relay	Joseph Henry	American
1835	photography (on paper)	William Fox Talbot	British
1835	ship's screw propeller	John Ericsson	Swedish
1836	stroboscope	Joseph Plateau	Belgian
1837	electroplating	Moritz von Jacobi/ George Elkington	German-born Russian/ British
1838	single-wire telegraph	Samuel Morse	American

Key Inventions

Year	Invention	Inventor(s)	Inventor's nationality
1838	stereoscope	Charles Wheatstone	British
1839	treadle bicycle	Kirkpatrick Macmillan	Scottish
1839	calotype	William Fox Talbot	British
1839	daguerreotype	Louis Daguerre	French
1839	photoelectric cell	Antoine Becquerel	French
1839	steam hammer	James Nasmyth	British
1839	vulcanized rubber	Charles Goodyear	America
1840	electric clock	Alexander Bain	Scottish
1844	aneroid barometer	Lucien Vidi	French
1844	steam foghorn	J N Taylor	British
1845	guncotton	Christian Schönbein	German
1845	single-needle telegraph	Charles Wheatstone and William Cooke	British
1846	hydraulic crane	William Armstrong	British
1846	sewing machine	Elias Howe	American
1846	printing telegraph	Royal House	American
1847	rotary printing press	Richard Hoe	American
1848	chewing gum	John Curtis	American
1848	diving bell	James Eads	American
1848	model steam airplane	John Stringfellow	British
1849	pressure gauge	Eigène Bourdon	French
1849	reinforced concrete	Joseph Monier	French
1849	safety pin	Walter Hunt	American
1850	electric locomotive	Charles Page	American
1850	ophthalmoscope	Hermann Helmholtz	German
1851	arch-truss bridge	Daniel McCallum	Scottish-born American

Key Inventions

Year	Invention	Inventor(s)	Inventor's nationality
1851	mechanical refrigerator	John Gorrie	American
1851	sewing machine	Isaac Singer	American
1852	gyroscope	Léon Foucault	French
1852	safety elevator	Elisha Otis	American
1852	steerable airship	Henri Giffard	French
1853	man-carrying glider	George Cayley	British
1854	automatic revolver	Horace Smith and Daniel Wesson	American
1855	compressor refrigerator	James Harrison	Scottish-born Australian
1855	mercury vacuum pump	Heinrich Geissler	German
1855	rotary cultivator	Robert Romaine	Canadian
1855	safety match	Johan Lundström	Swedish
1855	seismograph	Luigi Palmieri	Italian
1856	aniline dyes	William Perkin	British
1857	steam plow	John Fowler	British
1858	can opener	Ezra Warner	American
1858	gas discharge tube	Heinrich Geissler	German
1859	gas-burning internal combustion engine	Etienne Lenoir	French
1859	lead-acid accumulator	Gaston Planté	French
1860	ship's armor plating	John Brown	British
1861	jackhammer	Germain Sommelier	French
1861	pedal bicycle	Pierre and Ernest Michaux	French
1862	ball bearings	Pierre Michaux	French
1862	rapid-fire machine gun	Richard Gatling	American

Key Inventions

Year	Invention	Inventor(s)	Inventor's nationality
1863	pasteurization	Louis Pasteur	French
1863	roller skates	James Plimpton	American
1865	cylinder lock	Linus Yale	American
1866	cable car	Wilhelm Ritter	German
1866	dynamite	Alfred Nobel	Swedish
1866	indelible pencil	Edson Clark	American
1866	self-propelled torpedo	Robert Whitehead	British
1866	zinc-carbon battery	Georges Leclanché	French
1867	barbed wire	Lucien Smith	American
1867	railroad air brake	George Westinghouse	American
1867	modern typewriter	Christopher Scholes	American
1867	water-tube boiler	George Babcock and Stephen Wilcox	American
1868	celluloid	John Hyatt	American
1868	explosive harpoon	Svend Foyn	Norwegian
1869	margarine	Hippolyte Mergé-Mouriès	French
1869	ticker-tape machine	Thomas Edison	American
1870	penny-farthing bicycle	Pierre Lallement	French
1872	industrial dynamo	Zénobe Gramme	Belgian
1876	four-stroke internal combustion engine	Nikolaus Otto	German
1876	telephone	Alexander Graham Bell	American
1876	safety bicycle	James Starley	British
1877	electric light bulb	Thomas Edison/ Joseph Swan	American/ British
1878	microphone	David Hughes	American

Key Inventions

Year	Invention	Inventor(s)	Inventor's nationality
1879	electric arc furnace	William Siemens	German-born British
1879	steam turbine	Carl de Laval	Swedish
1880	bolometer	Samuel Langley	American
1881	gasoline-engine tractor	John Froel	American
1883	automatic machine gun	Hiram Maxim	American
1884	fountain pen	Lewis Waterman	American
1884	gas-engine car	Gottlieb Daimler	German
1884	linotype machine	Ottmar Mergenthaler	American
1884	rack railway	Roman Abt	Swiss
1884	rayon	Hilaire de Chardonnet	French
1885	dictaphone	Charles Tainter	American
1885	gas mantle	Carl von Welsbach	Austrian
1885	motorcycle	Gottlieb Daimler	German
1885	spark plug	Etienne Lenoir	French
1885	transformer	William Stanley	American
1886	Coca-Cola	John Pemberton	American
1886	flush toilet	Thomas Crapper	British
1886	gasoline-engine car	Karl Benz	German
1886	steam car	Ransom Olds	American
1887	monotype machine	Tolbert Landston	American
1887	phonograph record	Emile Berliner	German-American
1888	AC electric motor	Nikola Tesla	Croatian-born American
1888	pneumatic tire	John Dunlop	Scottish

Key Inventions

Year	Invention	Inventor(s)	Inventor's nationality
1888	photographic film	George Eastman	American
1889	jukebox	Louis Glass	American
1889	movie camera	William Friese-Greene	British
1890	magneto	Robert Bosch	German
1891	man-carrying glider	Otto Lillienthal	German
1892	electric furnace	Henri Moissan	French
1892	escalator	Jesse Reno	American
1892	vacuum bottle	James Dewar	Scottish
1893	magnetic wire recorder	Valdemar Poilsen	Danish
1893	zipper	Whitcombe Judson	American
1894	wheat flakes	John Kellogg	American
1895	diesel engine	Rudolf Diesel	German
1895	motion pictures	Lumière brothers	French
1895	safety razor	King Gillette	American
1897	car radiator	Wilhelm Maybach	German
1897	cathode-ray tube	Karl Braun	German
1897	steam-turbine boat	Charles Parsons	British
1898	Pepsi-Cola	Caleb Bradman	American
1899	aspirin	Felix Hoffmann	German
1900	twin-hulled hydrofoil	Enrico Forlanini	Italian
1900	paper-clip	Johaan Vaaler	Norwegian
1901	radio	Guglielmo Marconi	Italian
1902	disk brake	Frederick Lanchester	British
1902	electric typewriter	Geroge Blickensderfer	American
1903	airplane	Wright brothers	American
1903	car seat belt	Gustave Liebau	French
1903	electrocardiograph	Wilhelm Einthoven	Dutch

Key Inventions

Year	Invention	Inventor(s)	Inventor's nationality
1904	diode vacuum tube	John Fleming	British
1906	radio broadcasting	Reginald Fessenden	American
1906	rigid airship	Ferdinand von Zeppelin	German
1906	triode vacuum tube	Lee De Forest	American
1907	Bakelite	Leo Baekland	Belgian-American
1907	helicopter	Breguet brothers	French
1908	cellophane	Charles Cross	British
1908	gyrocompass	Hermann Anschütz-Kampfe	German
1908	tungsten-filament lamp	William Coolidge	American
1910	neon lighting	Georges Claude	French
1912	teleprinter	Frederick Creed	Canadian
1913	Geiger counter	Hans Geiger	German
1915	hand grenade	William Mills	British
1915	military tank	Ernest Swinton	British
1916	sonar	Paul Langevin	French
1919	mass spectrograph	Francis Aston	British
1923	autogyro	Juan de la Cierva	Spanich
1923	iconoscope TV tube	Vladimir Zworikin	Russian-born American
1925	mechanical television	John Logie Baird	Scottish
1925	Scotch tape	Richard Drew	American
1926	aerosol can	Erik Rotheim	Norwegian
1926	liquid-fueled rocket	Robert Goddard	American
1928	iron lung	Philip Drinker	American
1928	magnetic tape recorder	Fritz Pfleumer	German

Key Inventions

Year	Invention	Inventor(s)	Inventor's nationality
1931	high-voltage generator	Robert Van de Graaff	American
1931	gyroscopic stabilizer	Elmer Sperry	American
1932	cyclotron	Ernest Lawrence	American
1933	FM radio	Edwin Armstrong	American
1935	parking meter	Carlton Magee	American
1935	radar	Robert Watson-Watt/ Rudolf Künold	British/ German
1937	jet engine	Frank Whittle	British
1937	nylon	Wallace Carruthers	American
1938	ballpoint pen	Lazlo Biro	Hungarian
1938	electron microscope	Ernst Ruska	German
1942	aqualung	Jacques Cousteau	French
1943	kidney machine	Willem Kolff	Dutch-born American
1945	synchrocyclotron	Vladimir Veksler	Russian
1947	Polaroid camera	Edwin Land	American
1948	bathyscaphe	Auguste Piccard	Swiss
1948	holography	Dennis Gabor	Hungarian born British
1948	junction transistor	William Shockley	American
1948	LP phonograph record	Peter Goldmark	American
1951	field-ion microscope	Erwin Mueller	German-born American
1953	heart-lung machine	John Gibbon	American
1953	maser	Charles Townes	American
1954	non-stick pan	Marc Gregoire	French

Key Inventions

Year	Invention	Inventor(s)	Inventor's nationality
1956	videotape recorder	Alexander Poniatoff	Russian-born American
1957	artificial pacemaker	Earl Bakken	American
1959	hovercraft	Christopher Cockerell	British
1960	ruby laser	Theodore Maiman	American
1963	CAT scanner	Allan Cormack	South African-born American
1964	music synthesizer	Robert Moog	American
1966	fiber-optic cable	Charles Kao and George Hockham	British
1968	computer mouse	Douglas Engelbart	American
1970	light-emitting diode	F Hoffman	Swiss
1971	microprocessor	Ted Hoff	American
1976	videocassette recorder	Shizuo Takano	Japanese
1978	scanning ion microscope	Robert Seliger	American
1981	scanning tunneling microscope	Gerd Binnig and Heinrich Rohrer	Swiss
1982	artificial heart	Robert Jarvik	American
1985	atomic force microscope	Gerd Binnig	Swiss

57. Life expectancy by country

Countries with highest life expectancy at birth (given in years):

Men	Expectancy	Women	Expectancy
Luxembourg	77.9	Japan	83.6
Japan	77.0	Switzerland	81.9
Sweden	76.5	France	81.6
Iceland	76.2	Sweden	81.5
Switzerland	75.7	Australia	81.1
Greece	75.6	Norway	81.1
Norway	75.4	Canada	80.9
Israel	75.3	Italy	80.7
Australia	75.2	Belgium	80.6
Malta	74.9	Iceland	80.6

Countries with lowest life expectancy at birth (given in years):

Men	Expectancy	Women	Expectancy
Sierra Leone	40	Sierra Leone	43
Uganda	42	Uganda	44
Guinea-Bissau	44	Malawi	45
Malawi	44	Afghanistan	46
Afghanistan	45	Gambia	47
Burkina Faso	45	Guinea	47
Gambia	45	Guinea-Bissau	47
Mozambique	45	Zambia	47
Rwanda	45	Burkina Faso	48
Zambia	45	Mozambique	48

58. Major causes of death worldwide

Cause	No. deaths per year	% of all deaths
cardiovascular disease	7,380,000	13.3
cancer	7,230,000	13.0
cerebrovascular disease	5,110,000	9.2
lung infections	3,450,000	6.3
HIV/AIDS	2,290,000	4.1
obstructive lung disease	2,250,000	4.0
diarrhea and dysentery	2,220,000	4.0
children's diseases	1,650,000	3.0
tuberculosis	1,500,000	2.7
accidents	1,170,000	2.1

59. Average heights and weights of men and women (worldwide)

	MEN		
	Height		Weight
(cm)	(ft in.)	(kg)	(lb)
155	5 1	56	123
158	5 2	58	128
160	5 3	59	130
163	5 4	60	132
165	5 5	62	136
168	5 6	64	141
170	5 7	66	145
173	5 8	68	149
175	5 9	69	153
178	5 10	72	158
180	5 11	74	163
183	6 0	76	167
185	6 1	78	172
188	6 2	80	176
191	6 3	82	180

Average heights and weights of men and women (worldwide)

WOMEN

Height		Weight	
(cm)	(ft in.)	(kg)	(lb)
142	4 8	46	102
145	4 9	47	104
147	4 10	49	107
150	4 11	50	110
152	5 0	51	113
155	5 1	53	116
158	5 2	54	120
160	5 3	56	123
163	5 4	58	128
165	5 5	60	132
168	5 6	62	136
170	5 7	64	141
173	5 8	65	143
175	5 9	67	147
178	5 10	69	152

60. Energy requirements of men and women

Men:

Activity	Energy required	
	(kJ/hour)	*(kcal/hour)*
sleeping	250	60
sitting	350	85
standing	500	145
walking on the level	925	220
walking uphill	1850	440
running on the level	2500	600
running uphill	3150	750

Women:

Activity	Energy required	
	(kJ/hour)	*(kcal/hour)*
sleeping	225	55
sitting	300	70
standing	450	105
walking on the level	750	180
walking uphill	1510	360
running on the level	1800	430
running uphill	2200	525

61. Number of adherents of religions

Religion	No. of members (millions)	Comments
Baha'ism	5.8	Originated and practiced mainly in Iran
Buddhism	362	Consisting of 56% Mahayana, 38% Theravada, 6% Tantrayana
Christianity	2015	50% Roman Catholic, 20.5% Protestant, 11% Orthodox, 3.5% Anglican, 15% Other
Confucianism	5	Largest number of members in China
Hinduism	786	70% Vaishnavites, 25% Shaivites, 5% Other
Islam	1215	83% Sunnites, 16% Shi'ites, 1% Other
Jainism	3	Practiced in parts of India
Judaism	18	Some 48% in the USA, 30% in Israel, 30% in Europe (including Russia)
Shinto	3	Native religion of Japan
Sikhism	16	Members found mainly in Punjab, India
Tribal religions	256	Practiced in Africa, Asia and Oceania

62. Greek and Roman gods

Greek	Roman equivalent	Association
Aphrodite	Venus	love
Apollon	Apollo	Sun
Ares	Mars	war
Artemis	Diana	Moon/hunting
Athene	Minerva	wisdom
Demeter	Ceres	agriculture
Dionysus	Bacchus	wine
Eileithyia	Lucina	birth
Eros	Cupid	love
Hephaestus	Vulcan	smith
Hera	Juno	queen
Hermes	Mercury	messenger
Hestia	Vesta	hearth/home
Kronos	Saturn	time
Nike	Victoria	victory
Persephone	Prosperina	underworld
Pluton	Pluto	underworld
Poseidon	Neptune	ocean
Tyche	Fortuna	luck
Zephyr	Favonius	west wind
Zeus	Jupiter	king

63. Books of the Bible

Old Testament:

Book	Abbreviation	Book	Abbreviation
Genesis	Gen.	Ecclesiastes	Eccles.
Exodus	Exod.	Song of Solomon	S. of S.
Leviticus	Lev.	Isaiah	Isa.
Numbers	Num.	Jeremiah	Jer.
Deuteronomy	Deut.	Lamentations	Lam.
Joshua	Josh.	Ezekiel	Ezek.
Judges	Judg.	Daniel	Dan.
Ruth	Ruth	Hosea	Hos.
I. Samuel	I Sam.	Joel	Joel
II. Samuel	II Sam.	Amos	Amos
I. Kings	I Kgs.	Obadiah	Obad.
II. Kings	II Kgs.	Jonah	Jonah
I. Chronicles	I Chr.	Micah	Mic.
II. Chronicles	II Chr.	Nahum	Nahum
Ezra	Ezra	Habakkuk	Hab.
Nehemiah	Neh.	Zephaniah	Zeph.
Esther	Esther	Haggai	Hag.
Job	Job	Zechariah	Zech.
Psalms	Ps.	Malachi	Mal.
Proverbs	Prov.		

Books of the Bible

New Testament:

Book	Abbreviation	Book	Abbreviation
Matthew	Matt.	I. Timothy	I Tim.
Mark	Mark	II. Timothy	II Tim.
Luke	Luke	Titus	Titus
John	John	Philemon	Philem.
The Acts	Acts	To the Hebrews	Heb.
The Romans	Rom.	Epistle of James	Jas.
I. Corinthians	I Cor.	I. Peter	I Pet.
II. Corinthians	II Cor.	II. Peter	II Pet.
Galatians	Gal.	I. John	I John
Ephesians	Eph.	II. John	II John
Philippians	Phil.	III. John	III John
Colossians	Col.	Jude	Jude
I. Thessalonians	I Thess.	Revelation	Rev.
II. Thessalonians	II Thess.		

Apocrypha:

Book	Abbreviation
I. Esdras	I Esd.
II. Esdras	II Esd.
Tobit	Tobit
Judith	Judith
The Rest of Esther	Rest of Esth.
The Wisdom of Solomon	Wisd.
Ecclesiasticus	Ecclus.
Baruch, with the Epistle of Jeremiah	Baruch
The Song of the Three Holy Children	S. of III Ch.
The History of Susanna	Sus.
Bel and the Dragon	Bel & Dr.
The Prayer of Manasses	Pr. of Man.
I. Maccabees	I Macc.
II. Maccabees	II Macc.

64. Twelve tribes of Israel, seven sacraments, twelve apostles, etc.

Twelve Tribes of Israel:

Name	Origin
Reuben Levi Judah Issachar Zebulun	sons of Jacob and Leah (Jacob's first wife)
Gad Asher	sons of Jacob and Zilpah (Leah's maidservant)
Benjamin	son of Jacob and Rachel (Jacob's second wife)
Dan Naphtali	sons of Jacob and Bilhah (Rachel's maidservant)
Manasseh Ephraim	sons of Joseph (who was a son of Jacob and Rachel)

Twelve tribes of Israel, seven sacraments, twelve apostles, etc.

Seven sacraments:

Baptism

Confirmation

Eucharist

Penance

Anointing the Sick

Ordination

Matrimony

Twelve apostles:

Andrew

James

Philip

Matthew (Levi)

James, son of Alphaeus

Judas Iscariot

Peter (Simon)

John

Nathaniel (Bartholomew)

Thomas

Judas, brother of James

Simon the Zealot

Twelve tribes of Israel, seven sacraments, twelve apostles, etc.

Ten Commandments (wording varies):

1. I am the Lord thy God. Thou shall have no other gods before me.

2. Thou shall not make unto thee any graven image, or any likeness of anything that is in heaven above, or that is in the earth beneath, or that is in the water under the earth.

3. Thou shall not take the name of the Lord thy God in vain.

4. Remember the Sabbath day to keep it holy.

5. Honor thy father and mother.

6. Thou shall not kill.

7. Thou shall not commit adultery.

8. Thou shall not steal.

9. Thou shall not bear false witness against thy neighbor.

10. Thou shall not covet thy neighbor's house, thou shall not covet thy neighbor's wife, nor his manservant, nor his maidservant, nor his ox, nor his ass, nor anything that is thy neighbor's.

Seven deadly sins:

Avarice

Envy

Gluttony

Lust

Pride

Sloth

Wrath

65. Clothing sizes

Coat sizes:

	Men			Women	
US size	UK size	European	US size	UK size	European
34	34	44	8	30	36
36	36	46	10	32	38
38	38	48	12	34	40
40	40	50	14	36	42
42	42	52	16	38	44
44	44	54	18	40	46
46	46	56	20	42	48
48	48	58			

Shirt and blouse sizes:

	Men			Women	
US size	UK size	European	US size	UK size	European
13	13	30-31	30	32	38
13½	13½	32-33	32	34	40
14	14	34-35	34	36	42
14½	14½	36-37	36	38	44
15	15	38	38	40	46
15½	15½	39-40	40	42	48
16	16	41	41	44	50
16½	16½	42	44	46	52
17	17	43	46	48	54
17½	17½	44-45			

Clothing sizes

Shoe sizes:

	Men			Women	
US size	UK size	European	US size	UK size	European
7	6½	38-39	4	2½	32-25
7½	7	40	5	3½	35-36
8	7½	41	6	4½	36-38
8½	8	42	7	5½	38-39
9	8½	43	8	6½	40
9½	9	43-44	9	7½	41-42
10	9½	44	10	8½	42-44
10½	10	45			
11	10½	45-46			
11½	11	47			
12	11½	47-48			

Women's clothes:

US size	UK size	European
6	8	36
8	10	38
10	12	40
12	14	42
14	16	44
16	18	46
18	20	48
20	22	50
22	24	52

Clothing sizes

Children's clothes:

US size	UK size	European
2	16–18	40–45
4	20–22	50–55
6	24–26	60–65
7	28–30	70–75
8	32–34	80–85
9	36–38	90–95

Children's shoes:

US size	UK size	European
1	1	17
2	2	18
3	3	19
4	4	20
4½	4½	21
5	5	22
6	6	23
7	7	24
8	8	25
8½	8½	26
9	9	27
10	10	28
11	11	29
12	12	30
12½	12½	31
13	13	32

66. Paper sizes

Traditional sizes (dimensions may vary slightly):

Name	Dimensions	
	(inches)	*(millimeters)*
emperor	48 x 72	1220 x 1830
antiquarian	31 x 53	785 x 1345
double elephant	27 x 40	685 x 1015
atlas	26 x 34	660 x 865
colombier	23½ x 34½	595 x 875
imperial	22 x 30	560 x 760
elephant	23 x 28	585 x 710
cartridge	21 x 26	535 x 660
double crown	20 x 30	510 x 760
super royal	19 x 27	480 x 685
royal	20 x 25	510 x 635
small royal	19 x 25	480 x 635
medium	17½ x 22	445 x 560
large post	16½ x 21	420 x 535
copy or draft	16 x 20	405 x 510
demy	15½ x 22½	395 x 570
post	15¼ x 19	385 x 480
foolscap	13½ x 17	340 x 430
brief	13¼ x 16½	335 x 420
pot(t)	12½ x 15	310 x 380

Paper sizes

'Metric' sizes:

Name	Dimensions (millimeters)
metric royal	960 x 1,272
metric demy	888 x 1,128
metric large crown	816 x 1,056
metric crown	768 x 1,008

International (ISO) sizes:
A series:

	millimeters	inches equivalent
A0	841 x 1,189	33⅛ x 46¾
A1	594 x 841	23⅜ x 33⅛
A2	420 x 594	16½ x 23⅜
A3	297 x 420	11¾ x 16½
A4	210 x 297	8¼ x 11¾
A5	148 x 210	5⅞ x 8¼
A6	105 x 148	4⅛ x 5⅞
A7	74 x 105	2⅞ x 4⅛
A8	52 x 74	2 x 2⅞
A9	37 x 52	1½ x 2
A10	26 x 37	1 x 1½

Paper sizes

B series:

	millimeters	inches equivalent
B0	1,000 x 1,414	39⅜ x 55⅝
B1	707 x 1,000	27⅞ x 39⅜
B2	500 x 707	19⅝ x 27⅞
B3	353 x 500	13⅞ x 19⅝
B4	250 x 353	9⅞ x 13⅞
B5	176 x 250	7 x 9⅞
B6	125 x 176	4⅞ x 7
B7	88 x 125	3½ x 4⅞
B8	62 x 88	2½ x 3½
B9	44 x 62	1¾ x 2½
B10	31 x 44	1¼ x 1¾

The **C series** sizes are used for envelopes and folders designed to hold the A series sizes. For example:

	millimeters	inches equivalent	
C4	229 x 324	9 x 12¾	holds A4 flat
C5	162 x 229	6⅜ x 9	holds A4 folded in half or A5 flat
C6	114 x 162	4½ x 6⅜	holds A4 folded in four, A5 folded in half or A6 flat
DL	220 x 110	8⅝ x 4⅜	holds A4 folded twice, in thirds

67. Standard contents of bottles

Name	Capacity		
	(liters)	(fluid ounces)	(pints)
wine bottle	0.75	25.25	1.58
magnum	1.50	50.72	3.17
jeroboam	3.0	101.4	6.34
rehoboam	4.5	152.2	9.51
methuselah	6.0	202.9	12.68
salmanazar	9.0	304.3	19.02
balthazar	12.0	405.8	25.36
nebuchadnezzar	15.0	507.2	31.70

68. Alcoholic content of some drinks

1 unit is equivalent to 10 milliliters (0.338 fluid ounces) of pure alcohol

Type of drink	Alcohol (%)	Alcohol (units/liter)
beer	2	1.0
	3	4.0
	5	5.3
	6	8.0
wine	5	5.3
	7	7.3
	9	9.3
	11	10.7
	13	13.3
	15	15.3
fortified wine	15	15.3
(sherry, etc.)	17	17.3
	20	20.2
	23	23.3
	25	25.3
	27	27.4
spirits	37	37.5
	38	38.6
	40	40.7
	43	43.9
	45	46.0

69. Composition and energy content of common foods

Food	Protein (%)	Fat (%)	Carbohydrate (%)	Energy (kJ/kg)	Energy (kcal/kg)
almonds	19.0	54.0	54.0	23,650	5650
apples	0.3	0.0	11.5	2135	510
apricots	4.0	0.5	36.5	6750	1610
avocados	2.0	19.5	1.9	7850	1875
bacon (fried)	24.5	53.5	0.0	22,850	5460
bananas	1.0	0.0	19	3475	830
beef (roast)	26.5	12.5	0.0	9400	2250
beef steak (grilled)	30.0	12.0	0.0	9100	2180
beets (boiled)	2.5	0.0	9.5	1950	470
blackberries	1.2	0.0	6.5	1350	320
brown bread	8.5	2.0	44.3	9250	2200
butter	0.2	83	0.0	30,300	7250
cabbage (boiled)	0.7	0.0	1.2	375	90
carrots (boiled)	0.5	0.0	4.4	835	200
celery	1.0	0.0	1.2	375	90
cheese (Brie)	19.0	23.0	2.0	13,200	3150
cheese (Cheddar)	25.5	34.5	22.0	17,050	4075
cheese (cottage)	13.7	4.0	2.4	4130	1000
cherries	0.9	0.1	11.5	2050	500
chicken (roast)	29.5	7.0	0.0	7950	1900
chick peas	20.0	6.0	50.0	13,400	3200
chocolate	4.0	29.0	63.0	21,350	5100
cornflakes	11	5.0	80	17,350	4150

Composition and energy content of common foods

Food	Protein (%)	Fat (%)	Carbohydrate (%)	Energy (kJ/kg)	(kcal/kg)
corn on the cob	3.0	1.0	21.0	3750	900
crackers (sweet)	7.0	23.0	62.0	20,300	4850
cream	2.5	19.0	4.1	8170	1950
dates	2.0	1.0	73.0	9,000	2150
eggplant	1.0	0.4	2.2	650	155
eggs (boiled)	12.5	11.5	1.5	6750	1620
grapefruit	0.8	0.1	6.9	1250	300
grapes	0.5	0.0	15.5	2700	650
ham (no fat)	22.0	5.0	0.0	7100	1700
honey	0.0	0.0	71.0	12,500	2950
lettuce	1.0	0.0	1.8	500	120
lamb chop (grilled)	24.0	29.0	0.0	14,900	3530
liver (fried)	29.0	16.0	4.0	11,900	2850
lobster	20.0	3.0	0.0	5000	1200
mangoes	0.7	0.2	14.0	2450	585
margarine (polyunsat.)	0.2	81.5	1.0	30,400	7265
melon	0.6	0.1	6.5	1200	285
milk (non-skim)	3.3	3.6	4.8	2800	670
mushrooms	1.8	0.5	0.5	550	130
mussels	17.0	1.0	0.0	3550	850
olive oil	0.0	100	0.0	37,650	9000
oranges	0.6	0.0	8.5	1600	380
pasta (boiled)	3.6	0.7	22.2	4400	1050

Composition and energy content of common foods

Food	Protein (%)	Fat (%)	Carbohydrate (%)	Energy (kJ/kg)	(kcal/kg)
peaches	1.0	0.1	14.0	1400	335
peanuts	28.0	49.0	8.5	25,500	6100
pears	0.3	0.1	10.0	1700	405
peas (boiled)	6.0	0.9	9.5	2900	695
pineapple	0.0	0.0	14.0	1900	460
pork chop (grilled)	28.0	24.0	0.0	13,800	3300
potatoes (boiled)	1.5	0.0	20.0	3650	875
rice (boiled)	5.6	1.0	35.5	5900	1400
spinach (boiled)	5.0	0.0	1.5	1150	275
strawberries	0.8	0.1	6.0	1150	275
sugar	0.0	0.0	100	17,150	4100
tomatoes	1.0	0.0	3.0	625	150
tuna (canned)	28.0	1.0	0.0	4800	1150
turkey (roast)	36.0	3.0	0.0	5850	1400
walnuts	15.0	64.0	16.0	22,000	5250
white bread	8.4	1.9	49.3	10,000	2400
white fish (steamed)	22.5	0.8	0.0	420	100
zucchini	1.8	0.4	1.8	750	180

70. US road distances

	Distance from New York		Distance from San Francisco	
	(km)	(miles)	(km)	(miles)
Atlanta, Georgia	1370	850	4000	2485
Augusta, Maine	820	510	5450	3385
Dallas, Texas	2515	1560	2820	1750
Boston, Massachusetts	340	210	5050	3135
Chicago, Illinois	1305	810	3500	2175
Columbus, Ohio	905	560	3920	2435
Jacksonville, Florida	1530	950	4435	2750
Juneau, Alaska	4595	2850	3130	1000
Indianapolis, Indiana	1175	730	3695	2295
Las Vegas, Nevada	4145	2575	920	570
Little Rock, Arkansas	2015	1255	3630	2255
Nashville, Tennessee	1450	900	3760	2335
New York City, New York	—	—	4725	2935
Pheonix, Arizona	3950	2455	1225	760
Portland, Oregon	4695	2910	1030	640
Salt Lake City, Utah	3530	2195	1210	750
San Francisco, California	4735	2935	—	—
Washington, D.C.	385	240	4580	2845

71. European road distances

	Distance from London*		Distance from Athens	
	(km)	(miles)	(km)	(miles)
Amsterdam, the Netherlands	550	340	2970	1845
Athens, Greece	1990	3200	—	—
Belgrade, Serbia	2030	1260	725	450
Berlin, Germany	1170	725	1535	955
Berne, Switzerland	970	600	1565	975
Brussels, Belgium	390	240	1745	1085
Bucharest, Romania	2590	1610	805	500
Budapest, Hungary	1770	1100	1015	630
Copenhagen, Denmark	1310	815	1790	1110
Dublin, Ireland	550	340	2445	1520
Frankfurt, Germany	800	500	1570	975
Helsinki, Finland	2380	1480	2430	1510
Lisbon, Portugal	1315	1445	2430	1750
London, UK	—	—	1990	1235
Luxembourg	375	230	1615	1005
Madrid	1040	645	2410	1500
Oslo, Norway	1195	740	2150	1335
Paris, France	280	175	1825	1135
Prague, Czech Republic	815	505	1325	825
Rome, Italy	1125	700	1520	945
Stockholm, Sweden	1205	750	2155	1340
Tallinn, Estonia	1735	1075	2055	1280
Vienna, Austria	940	580	1125	700
Warsaw, Poland	1075	670	1400	870
Zagreb, Croatia	1025	635	970	600
Zürich, Switzerland	640	400	1625	1010

* Including shortest sea crossing

72. Time differences

Around the USA:

Times in major US cities when it is 12.00 noon, Eastern Standard Time

City	Time
Anchorage	06.00
Atlanta	12.00
Austin	11.00
Boston	12.00
Chicago	11.00
Columbus	12.00
Dallas	11.00
Denver	10.00
Honolulu	06.00
Indianapolis	12.00
Little Rock	11.00
Los Angeles	09.00
Miami	12.00
New Orleans	11.00
New York	12.00
Phoenix	10.00
Sacramento	09.00
Salt Lake City	10.00
San Francisco	09.00
Santa Fe	10.00
Topeka	11.00
Washington DC	12.00

Time differences

Around the world:

Times in major cities throughout the world when it is 12.00 noon, Greenwich Mean Time (GMT) or 12.00 noon Eastern Standard Time (EST).

City	Country	Time	
		(GMT)	**(EST)**
Adelaide	Australia	17.30	22.30
Addis Ababa	Ethiopia	15.00	20.00
Alexandria	Egypt	14.00	19.00
Algiers	Algeria	13.00	18.00
Amsterdam	The Netherlands	13.00	18.00
Ankara	Turkey	14.00	19.00
Athens	Greece	14.00	19.00
Auckland	New Zealand	23.00	04.00 (next day)
Baghdad	Iraq	15.00	19.00
Bangkok	Thailand	15.00	19.00
Barcelona	Spain	13.00	18.00
Beijing	China	20.00	01.00 (next day)
Belgrade	Serbia	13.00	18.00
Berlin	Germany	13.00	18.00

Time differences

City	Country	Time	
		(GMT)	(EST)
Bogotá	Colombia	07.00	12.00
Bombay	India	17.30	22.30
Brasilia	Brazil	09.00	14.00
Bremen	Germany	13.00	18.00
Brussels	Belgium	13.00	18.00
Bucharest	Romania	14.00	19.00
Budapest	Hungary	13.00	18.00
Bueos Aries	Argentina	09.00	14.00
Cairo	Egypt	14.00	19.00
Calcutta	India	17.30	22.30
Cape Town	South Africa	14.00	19.00
Caracas	Venezuela	08.00	13.00
Casablanca	Morocco	12.00	17.00
Chicago	USA	06.00	11.00
Colombo	Sri Lanka	17.30	22.30
Copenhagen	Denmark	13.00	18.00
Dakar	Senegal	12.00	17.00
Delhi	India	17.30	22.30

Time differences

City	Country	Time	
		(GMT)	(EST)
Dhaka	Bangladesh	18.00	23.00
Dublin	Ireland	12.00	17.00
Florence	Italy	13.00	18.00
Frankfurt	Germany	13.00	18.00
Gdansk	Poland	13.00	18.00
Geneva	Switzerland	13.00	18.00
Guatemala City	Guatemala	06.00	11.00
Halifax NS	Canada	08.00	13.00
Hanoi	Vietnam	19.00	24.00
Havana	Cuba	19.00	24.00
Helsinki	Finland	14.00	19.00
Hong Kong	China	20.00	01.00 (next day)
Honolulu	USA	02.00	07.00
Istanbul	Turkey	14.00	19.00
Jakarta	Indonesia	19.00	24.00
Jeddah	Saudi Arabia	15.00	20.00
Jerusalem	Israel	14.00	19.00

Time differences

City	Country	Time (GMT)	Time (EST)
Johannesburg	South Africa	14.00	19.00
Karachi	Pakistan	17.00	22.00
Kinshasa	Congo, Dem. Rep	11.00	16.00
Kuala Lumpur	Malaysia	20.00	01.00 (next day)
La Paz	Bolivia	08.0	13.00
Lima	Peru	07.00	12.00
Lisbon	Portugal	13.00	18.00
London	UK	12.00	17.00
Madrid	Spain	13.00	18.00
Managua	Nicaragua	06.00	11.00
Manlia	Philippines	20.00	01.00 (next day)
Mecca	Saudi Arabia	15.00	20.00
Melbourne	Australia	22.00	02.00 (next day)
Mexico City	Mexico	06.00	11.00
Monaco-Ville	Monaco	13.00	18.00
Montevideo	Uruguay	09.00	14.00

Time differences

City	Country	Time	
		(GMT)	(EST)
Montreal	Canada	07.00	12.00
Moscow	Russia	15.00	20.00
Munich	Germany	13.00	18.00
Nagasaki	Japan	21.00	02.00 (next day)
Nairobi	Nigeria	15.00	20.00
New Orleans	USA	06.00	11.00
New York	USA	07.00	12.00
Oslo	Norway	13.00	18.00
Ottawa	Canada	07.00	12.00
Panama City	Panama	07.00	12.00
Paris	France	13.00	18.00
Perth	Australia	20.00	01.00 (next day)
Port Moresby	Papua New Guinea	22.00	03.00 (next day)
Quito	Ecuador	07.00	12.00
Rangoon	Myanmar	18.30	3.30
Reykjavik	Iceland	12.00	17.00

Time differences

City	Country	Time	
		(GMT)	(EST)
Rio de Janeiro	Brazil	09.00	14.00
Riyadh	Saudi Arabia	15.00	20.00
Rome	Italy	13.00	18.00
St Petersburg	Russia	15.00	20.00
San Francisco	USA	04.00	09.00
San Juan	Costa Rica	08.00	13.00
Santiago	Chile	08.00	13.00
Seoul	South Korea	21.00	02.00 (next day)
Shanghai	China	20.00	01.00 (next day)
Singapore	Singapore	20.00	01.00 (next day)
Sofia	Bulgaria	14.00	19.00
Stockholm	Sweden	13.00	18.00
Sydney	Australia	22.00	02.00 (next day)
Tashkent	Uzbekistan	18.00	23.00
Teheran	Iran	15.30	20.30

Time differences

City	Country	Time	
		(GMT)	(EST)
Tel Aviv	Israel	14.00	19.00
Tokyo	Japan	21.00	02.00 (next day)
Toronto	Canada	07.00	12.00
Tripoli	Libya	13.00	18.00
Valparaiso	Chile	08.00	13.00
Vancouver	Canada	04.00	09.00
Vienna	Austria	13.00	18.00
Vladivostock	Russia	22.00	02.00 (next day)
Warsaw	Poland	13.00	18.00
Wellington	New Zealand	12.00 (midnight)	05.00 (next day)
Yokahama	Japan	21.00	02.00 (next day)
Zurich	Switzerland	13.00	18.00

73. Air distances (USA)

	Distance from New York City		Distance from San Francisco	
	(km)	(miles)	(km)	(miles)
Atlanta, Georgia	1205	750	3455	2145
Augusta, Maine	1075	665	4420	2745
Austin, Texas	2435	1515	2425	1510
Boston, Massachusetts	305	190	4360	2710
Chicago, Illinois	1160	1720	3000	1865
Columbus, Ohio	770	480	3415	2120
Juneau, Alaska	4590	2850	2440	1515
Honolulu, Hawaii	7995	4970	3840	2385
Indianapolis, Indiana	1045	650	3150	1955
Las Vegas, Nevada	3605	2240	675	420
Little Rock, Arkansas	1750	1085	2725	1690
Nashville, Tennessee	1225	760	3170	1970
New York City, New York	—	—	4155	2580
Phoenix, Arizona	3450	2145	1060	660
Salt Lake City, Utah	3185	1980	975	605
San Francisco, California	4155	2580	—	—
Santa Fe, New Mexico	2845	1765	1500	930
Washington, D.C.	330	205	3940	2450

74. Air distances (world)

	Distance from New York		Distance from Los Angeles	
	(km)	(miles)	(km)	(miles)
Beijing, China	11,000	6835	10,080	6265
Berlin, Germany	6385	3960	9325	5795
Bombay, India	12,565	7790	14,035	8700
Buenos Aires, Argentina	8550	5310	9870	6135
Calcutta, India	12,775	7940	13,145	8170
Cape Town, South Africa	12,580	7800	16,080	9970
Hong Kong, China	12,985	8070	11,680	7255
Honolulu, Hawaii	8000	4970	4130	2565
London, UK	5580	3465	8775	5450
Manila, Philippines	13,695	8510	11,725	7285
Melbourne, Australia	16,710	10,360	12,790	7930
Mexico City, Mexico	3370	2095	2485	1545
Moscow, Russia	7515	4670	9790	6085
Paris, France	5840	3630	9030	5610
Port Said, Egypt	9015	5590	12,145	7530
Quebec, Canada	709	440	4160	2580
Rio de Janeiro, Brazil	7775	4830	10,160	6315
Rome, Italy	6890	4280	10,210	6345
Santiago, Chile	8210	5100	8920	5540
Singapore	15,535	9650	14,145	8790
Tokyo, Japan	10,870	6755	8825	5480
Wellington, New Zealand	14,435	8970	10,825	6725

75. International car identification marks

Code	Country	Drive on the right (R) or left (L)?	Code	Country	Drive on the right (R) or left (L)?
A	Austria	R	DY	Benin	R
ADN	Yemen	R	DZ	Algeria	R
AFG	Afghanistan	R	E	Spain	R
AL	Albania	R	EAK	Kenya	L
AND	Andorra	R	EAT	Tanzania	L
AUS	Australia	L	EAU	Uganda	L
B	Belgium	R	EC	Ecuador	R
BD	Bangladesh	L	ES	El Salvador	R
BDS	Barbados	L	ET	Egypt	R
BG	Bulgaria	R	ETH	Ethiopia	R
BH	Belize	R	F	France	R
BR	Brazil	R	FJI	Fiji	L
BRN	Bahrain	R	FL	Liechtenstein	R
BRU	Brunei	L	FR	Faroe Islands	R
BS	Bahamas	L	GB	United Kingdom	L
BUR	Myanmar	R	GBA	Alderney	L
C	Cuba	R	GBG	Guernsey	L
CDN	Canada	R	GBJ	Jersey	L
CH	Switzerland	R	GBM	Isle of Man	L
CI	Côte d'Ivoire	R	GBl	Gibraltar	R
CL	Sri Lanka	L	GCA	Guatemala	R
CO	Colombia	R	GH	Ghana	R
CR	Costa Rica	R	GR	Greece	R
CS	Czech Republic	R	GUY	Guyana	L
CY	Cyprus	L	H	Hungary	R
D	Germany	R	HK	Hong Kong	L
DK	Denmark	R	HKJ	Jordan	R
DOM	Dominican Republic	R	I	Italy	R

International car identification marks

Code	Country	Drive on the right (R) or left (L)?	Code	Country	Drive on the right (R) or left (L)?
IL	Israel	R	PA	Panama	R
IND	India	L	PAK	Pakistan	L
IR	Iran	R	PE	Peru	R
IRL	Ireland	L	PL	Poland	R
IRQ	Iraq	R	PNG	Papua New Guinea	L
IS	Iceland	R	PY	Paraguay	R
J	Japan	L	RA	Argentina	R
JA	Jamaica	L	RB	Botswana	L
K	Kampuchea	R	RC	Taiwan	R
KWT	Kuwait	R	RCA	Central African Rep.	R
L	Luxembourg	R	RCB	Congo	R
LAD	Laos	R	RCH	Chile	R
LAR	Libya	R	RH	Haiti	R
LB	Liberia	R	RI	Indonesia	L
LS	Lesotho	L	RIM	Mauritania	R
M	Malta	L	RL	Lebanon	R
MA	Morocco	R	RM	Madagascar	R
MAL	Malaysia	L	RMM	Mali	R
MC	Monaco	R	RN	Niger	R
MEX	Mexico	R	RO	Romania	R
MS	Mauritius	L	ROK	Korea, Republic of	R
MW	Malawi	L	ROU	Uruguay	R
N	Norway	R	RP	Philippines	R
NA	Netherlands Antilles	R	RSM	San Marino	R
NIC	Nicaragua	R	RU	Burundi	R
NL	Netherlands	R			
Nl	New Zealand	L			
P	Portugal	R			

International car identification marks

Code	Country	Drive on the right (R) or left (L)?	Code	Country	Drive on the right (R) or left (L)?
RWA	Rwanda	R	V	Vatican City	R
S	Sweden	R	VN	Vietnam	R
SF	Finland	R	WAG	Gambia	R
SGP	Singapore	L	WAL	Sierra Leone	R
SME	Suriname	L	WAN	Nigeria	R
SN	Senegal	R	WO	Dominica	L
SWA	Namibia	L	WG	Grenada	L
SV	Seychelles	L	WL	St Lucia	L
SVR	Syria	R	WS	Samoa	R
T	Thailand	L	WV	St Vincent and the	
TG	Togo	R		Grenadines	L
TN	Tunisia	R	YV	Venezuela	R
TR	Turkey	R	Z	Zambia	L
TT	Trinidad and Tobago	L	ZA	South Africa	L
			ZRE	Zaire	R
USA	United States	R	ZW	Zimbabwe	L

76. States of the Union and data

State	Area		Capital	Date joined
	(sq km)	(sq miles)		the Union
Alabama	131,450	50,755	Montgomery	1819
Alaska	1,477,250	570,370	Juneau	1959
Arizona	294,350	113,650	Phoenix	1912
Arkansas	134,850	52,065	Little Rock	1836
California	403,950	155,965	Sacramento	1850
Colorado	268,650	103,725	Denver	1876
Connecticut	12,550	4845	Hartford	1788
Delaware	5050	1950	Dover	1787
Florida	139,850	53,995	Tallahassee	1845
Georgia	150,000	57,915	Atlanta	1788
Hawaii	16,650	6430	Honolulu	1959
Idaho	214,300	82,740	Boise	1890
Illinois	144,000	55,600	Springfield	1818
Indiana	92,900	35,870	Indianapolis	1816
Iowa	144,700	55,870	Des Moines	1846
Kansas	211,900	81,815	Topeka	1861
Kentucky	102,900	39,730	Frankfort	1792
Louisiana	112,850	43,570	Baton Rouge	1792

States of the Union and data

| State | Area | | Capital | Date joined |
	(sq km)	(sq miles)		the Union
Maine	79,950	30,870	Augusta	1812
Maryland	25,300	9770	Annapolis	1788
Massachusetts	20,300	7840	Boston	1788
Michigan	147,150	56,815	Lansing	1837
Minnesota	206,200	79,615	St Paul	1858
Mississippi	121,500	46,910	Jackson	1817
Missouri	178,450	68,890	Jefferson City	1821
Montana	380,850	147,050	Helena	1889
Nebraska	196,600	75,907	Lincoln	1867
Nevada	284,400	109,805	Carson City	1864
New Hampshire	23,250	8975	Concord	1788
New Jersey	19,200	7415	Trenton	1787
New Mexico	314,350	121,370	Santa Fe	1912
New York	122,300	47,220	Albany	1788
North Carolina	126,200	48,725	Raleigh	1789
North Dakota	178,700	68,995	Bismarck	1889
Ohio	106,050	40,945	Columbus	1803

States of the Union and data

State	Area		Capital	Date joined the Union
	(sq km)	(sq miles)		
Oklahoma	177,900	68,690	Oklahoma City	1907
Oregon	248,650	96,005	Salem	1858
Pennsylvania	116,100	44,825	Harrisburg	1837
Rhode Island	2700	1041	Providence	1790
South Carolina	78,000	30,115	Columbia	1788
South Dakota	199,750	77,125	Pierre	1889
Tennessee	106,750	41,215	Nashville	1796
Texas	678,350	261,910	Austin	1845
Utah	212,800	82,165	Salt Lake City	1896
Vermont	23,950	9245	Montpelier	1791
Virginia	102,550	39,595	Richmond	1788
Washington	172,450	66,585	Olympia	1889
West Virginia	62,400	24,095	Charleston	1863
Wisconsin	140,650	54,305	Madison	1848
Wyoming	251,500	97,105	Cheyenne	1890

77. US State codes

State	Abbreviation	Postal abbreviation	Area code
Alabama	Ala.	AL	205, 251, 256, 334
Alaska	—	AK	907
Arizona	Ariz.	AZ	480, 520, 602, 623, 928
Arkansas	Ark.	AR	479, 501, 870
California	Calif.	CA	209, 213, 310, 323, 408, 415, 510, 530, 559, 562, 619, 626, 650, 661, 707, 714, 760, 805, 818, 831, 858, 909, 916, 925, 949
Colorado	Colo.	CO	303, 719, 720, 970
Connecticut	Conn.	CT	203, 860
Delaware	Del.	DE	302
District of Columbia	D.C.	DC	202
Florida	Fla.	FL	239, 305, 321, 352, 386, 407, 561, 727, 754, 772, 786, 813, 850, 863, 904, 941, 954
Georgia	Ga.	GA	229, 404, 478, 678, 706, 770, 912
Hawaii	—	HI	808

US State codes

State	Abbreviation	Postal abbreviation	Area code
Idaho	Ida.	ID	208
Illinois	Ill.	IL	217, 224, 309, 312, 618, 630, 708, 773, 815, 847
Indiana	Ind.	IN	219, 260, 317, 574, 765, 812
Iowa	Ia.	IA	319, 515, 536, 641, 712
Kansas	Kans.	KA	316, 620, 785, 913
Kentucky	Ky.	KY	270, 502, 606, 859
Louisiana	La.	LA	225, 318, 337, 504, 985
Maine	Me.	ME	207
Maryland	Md.	MD	240, 301, 410, 443
Massachusetts	Mass.	MA	269, 339, 351, 413, 508, 617, 774, 781, 857, 978
Michigan	Mich.	MI	231, 248, 313, 517, 586, 616, 734, 810, 906, 947, 989
Minnesota	Minn.	MN	218, 320, 507, 612, 651, 763, 952
Mississippi	Miss.	MS	228, 601, 662

US State codes

State	Abbreviation	Postal abbreviation	Area code
Missouri	Mo.	MO	314, 417, 573, 636, 660, 816
Montana	Mont.	MT	406
Nebraska	Nebr.	NE	308, 402
Nevada	Nev.	NV	702, 775
New Hampshire	N.H.	NH	603
New Jersey	N.J.	NJ	201, 551, 609, 732, 848, 856, 862, 908, 973
New Mexico	N.Mex. or N.M.	NM	505
New York	N.Y.	NY	212, 315, 347, 516, 518, 585, 607, 631, 646, 716, 718, 845, 914, 917
North Carolina	N.C.	NC	252, 336, 704, 828, 910, 919, 980
North Dakota	N.Dak. or N.D.	ND	701
Ohio	O.	OH	216, 234, 419, 440, 513, 567, 614, 740 937
Oklahoma	Okla.	OK	405, 580, 918
Oregon	Ore.	OR	503, 541, 971

US State codes

State	Abbreviation	Postal abbreviation	Area code
Pennsylvania	Pa. or Penn.	PA	215, 267, 412, 484, 570, 610, 717, 724, 814, 878
Rhode Island	R.I.	RI	401
South Carolina	S.C.	SC	803, 843, 864
South Dakota	S.Dak. or S.D.	SD	605
Tennessee	Tenn.	TN	423, 615, 731, 865, 901, 931
Texas	Tex.	TX	210, 214, 254, 281, 361, 409, 469, 512, 682, 713, 806, 817, 830, 832, 903, 915, 936, 940, 956, 972, 979
Utah	Ut.	UT	435, 801
Vermont	Vt.	VT	802
Virginia	Va.	VA	276, 434, 540, 571, 703, 757, 804
Washington	Wash.	WA	206, 253, 360, 425, 509
West Virginia	W.Va.	WV	304
Wisconsin	Wis.	WI	262, 414, 608, 715, 920
Wyoming	Wyo.	WY	307

78. Canadian provinces, areas, and populations

Province	Area (sq kilometers)	(sq miles)	Population	Capital
Alberta	644,390	248,800	2,696,825	Edmonton
British Columbia	930,530	359,275	3,724,500	Victoria
Manitoba	650,000	250,970	1,113,900	Winnipeg
New Brunswick	72,090	27,835	738,135	Fredericton
Newfoundland	405,000	156,375	551,790	St John's
Northwest Territories	1,172,000	452,520	39,670	Yellowknife
Nova Scotia	52,840	20,400	909,280	Halifax
Nunavut	1,936,113	747,552	24,730	Iqaluit
Ontario	1,068,580	412,590	10,758,575	Toronto
Prince Edward Island	5655	2185	134,555	Charlottetown
Quebec	1,356,790	523,860	7,138,797	Quebec
Saskatchewan	651,900	251,705	990,235	Regina
Yukon Territory	483,450	186,665	30,765	Whitehorse

79. Mexican provinces, areas and populations

Province	Area		Population	Capital
	(sq kilometers)	(sq miles)		
Campeche	50,810	19,620	642,080	Campeche
Chiapas	74,210	28,655	3,584,790	Tuxtla
Chihuahua	244,940	94,570	2,792,990	Chihuahua
Coahuila	149,980	57,910	2,173,780	Saltillo
Durango	123,180	47,560	1,430,960	Durango
Guerrero	64,280	24,820	2,916,570	Chilpancingo
Jalisco	80,835	31,210	5,990,050	Guadalajara
México	21,355	8245	11,704,940	Toluca
Michoacán	59,930	23,140	3,870,600	Morelia
Nuevo Leon	64,925	25,065	3,086,470	Monterry
Oaxaca	93,950	36,275	3,224,270	Oaxaca
Puebla	33,900	13,090	4,624,360	Puebla
Quintana Roo	50,210	19,400	493,600	Chetumal
San Luis Potosí	63,070	24,350	2,191,790	San Luis Potosí
Sinaloa	58,330	22,520	2,425,670	Culiacán
Sonora	182,050	70,290	2,083,630	Hermosillo

Mexican provinces, areas and populations

Province	Area (sq kilometers)	(sq miles)	Population	Capital
Tabasco	25,265	9755	1,748,770	Villahermosa
Tamaulipas	79,384	30,650	2,527,330	Ciudad Victoria
Veracruz	71,700	27,685	6,734,550	Jalapa
Yucatan	38,400	14,825	1,558,620	Mérida
Zacatecas	75,040	28,975	1,336,250	Zacatecas

80. US military ranks

Grade	Air Force	Army
Enlisted ranks:		
E-1	Airman Basic	Private
E-2	Airman	Private 2
E-3	Airman First Class	Private First Class
E-4	Sergeant/Senior Airman	Corporal/Specialist
E-5	Staff Sergeant	Sergeant
E-6	Technical Sergeant	Staff Sergeant
E-7	Master Sergeant	Sergeant First Class
E-8	Senior Master Sergeant	First Sergeant/Master Sergeant
E-9	Chief Master Sergeant	Sergeant Major
E-10	Chief Master Sergeant of Air Force	Sergeant Major of the Army
Warrant Officers (not ranks in Air Force):		
W-1		Warrant Officer
W-2,3,4		Chief Warrant Officer
W-5		Master Warrant Officer

US military ranks

Grade	Air Force	Army
Commissioned Officers:		
O-1	Second Lieutenant	Second Lieutenant
O-2	First Lieutenant	First Lieutenant
O-3	Captain	Captain
O-4	Major	Major
O-5	Lieutenant Colonel	Lieutenant Colonel
O-6	Colonel	Colonel
O-7	Brigadier General	Brigadier General
O-8	Major General	Major General
O-9	Lieutenant General	Lieutenant General
O-10	General	General

Grade	Marine Corps	Navy and Coast Guard
Enlisted ranks:		
E-1	Private	Seaman Recruit
E-2	Private First Class	Seaman Apprentice
E-3	Lance Corporal	Seaman
E-4	Corporal	Petty Officer Third Class
E-5	Sergeant	Petty Officer Second Class
E-6	Staff Sergeant	Petty Officer First Class
E-7	Gunnery Sergeant	Chief Petty Officer
E-8	First Sergeant/ Master Sergeant	Senior Chief Petty Officer
E-9	Sergeant Major/Master Gunnery Sergeant	Master Chief Petty Officer
E-10	Sergeant Major of the Marines	Master Chief Petty Officer of the Navy

US military ranks

Grade	Marine Corps	Navy and Coast Guard
Warrant Officers:		
W-1	Warrant Officer	Warrant Officer
W-2,3,4	Chief Warrant Officer	Chief Warrant Officer
W-5	Master Warrant Officer	Master Warrant Officer
Commissioned Officers:		
O-1	Second Lieutenant	Ensign
O-2	First Lieutenant	Lieutenant Junior Grade
O-3	Captain	Lieutenant
O-4	Major	Lieutenant Commander
O-5	Lieutenant Colonel	Commander
O-6	Colonel	Captain
O-7	Brigadier General	Rear Admiral (lower half)
O-8	Major General	Rear Admiral (upper half)
O-9	Lieutenant General	Vice Admiral
O-10	General	Admiral

81. UK military ranks

Royal Navy	British Army	Royal Air Force
Seaman	Private	Aircraftman
Able Seaman	Lance Corporal	Corporal
Leading Seaman	Corporal	Sergeant
Petty Officer	Sergeant	Flight Sergeant
Chief Petty Officer	Staff Sergeant	Warrant Officer
Fleet Petty Officer	Warrant Officer	Acting Pilot Officer
Warrant Officer	Warrant Officer	Warrant Officer
Midshipman	Cadet	Cadet
	Second Lieutenant	Pilot Officer
Sublieutenant	Lieutenant	Flying Officer
Lieutenant	Captain	Flight Lieutenant
Lieutenant Commander	Major	Squadron Leader
Commander	Lieutenant Colonel	Wing Commander
Captain/Commodore	Colonel/Brigadier	Group Captain
		Air Commodore
Rear Admiral	Major General	Air Vice-Marshal
Vice-Admiral	Lieutenant General	Air Marshal
Admiral	General	Air Chief Marshal
Admiral of the Fleet	Field Marshal	Marshal of the RAF

82. World currencies

Nation	Currency unit	Subunits
Afghanistan	afghani	100 pule
Albania	lek	100 qindarka
Algeria	Algerian dinar	100 centimes
Andorra	euro	100 cents
Angola	kwanza	100 lwei
Antigua and Barbuda	East Caribbean dollar	100 cents
Argentina	peso	100 centavos
Armenia	dram	100 luma
Australia	Australian dollar	100 cents
Austria	euro	100 cents
Azerbaijan	manat	100 gopik
Bahamas	Bahamian dollar	100 cents
Bahrain	Bahraini dinar	1000 fils
Bangladesh	taka	100 poisha
Barbados	Barbadan dollar	100 cents
Belarus	ruble	100 kopecks
Belgium	euro	100 cents
Belize	Belize dollar	100 cents
Benin	CFA franc	100 centimes
Bhutan	ngultrum	100 chetrum
Bolivia	boliviano	100 centavos
Bosnia-Herzegovina	dinar	100 paras
Botswana	pula	100 thebe
Brazil	cruzeiro real	100 centavos

World currencies

Nation	Currency unit	Subunits
Brunei	Beunei dollar	100 cents
Bulgaria	lev	100 stotinki
Burkina Faso	CFA franc	100 centimes
Burundi	Burundi franc	100 centimes
Cambodia	riel	100 sen
Cameroon	CFA franc	100 centimes
Canada	Canadian dollar	100 cents
Cape Verde	escudo	100 centavos
Central African Rep.	CFE franc	100 centimes
Chad	CFA franc	100 centimes
Chile	peso	100 centesimos
China	yuan	10 jiao
Colombia	peso	100 centesimos
Comoros	CFA franc	100 centimes
Congo, Dem. Rep. of	zaïre	100 centimes
Congo, Rep. of	CFA franc	100 centimes
Costa Rica	colón	100 céntimos
Cote d'Ivoire	CFA franc	100 centimes
Croatia	kuna	100 paras
Cuba	peso	100 centavos
Cyprus	Cyprus pound	100 cents
Czech Republic	koruna	100 haleru
Denmark	krone	100 øre
Djibouti	franc	100 centimes

World currencies

Nation	Currency unit	Subunits
Dominica	East Caribbean dollar	100 cents
Dominican Republic	peso	100 centavos
Ecuador	sucre	100 centavos
Egypt	Egyptian pound	100 piastres
El Salvador	colón	100 centavos
Equatorial Guinea	CFA franc	100 centimes
Eritrea	birr	100 cents
Estonia	kroon	100 kopecks
Ethiopia	birr	100 cents
Fiji	Fiji dollar	100 cents
Finland	markka	100 pennia
France	euro	100 cents
Gabon	CFA franc	100 centimes
Gambia	dalasi	100 butut
Georgia	lari	100 kopecks
Germany	euro	100 cents
Ghana	cedi	100 pesewa
Greece	euro	100 cents
Grenada	East Caribbean dollar	100 cents
Guatemala	quetzal	100 centavos
Guinea	Guinean franc	100 centimes
Guinea-Bissau	peso	100 centavos
Guyana	Guyana dollar	100 cents
Haiti	gourde	100 centimes

World currencies

Nation	Currency unit	Subunits
Honduras	lempira	100 centavos
Hungary	forint	100 filler
Iceland	króna	100 aurar
India	rupee	100 paise
Indonesia	rupiah	100 sen
Iran	rial	100 dinars
Iraq	dinar	1000 fils
Ireland	euro	100 cents
Israel	sheqel	100 agorot
Italy	euro	100 cents
Japan	yen	100 sen
Jordan	dinar	1000 fils
Kazakstan	tenge	100 kopecks
Kenya	shilling	100 cents
Kiribati	Australian dollar	100 cents
Korea, North	won	100 chon
Korea, South	won	100 chon
Kuwait	dinar	1000 fils
Kyrgyzstan	som	100 tyiyn
Laos	kip	100 at
Latvia	lat	100 santami
Lebanon	Lebanese pound	100 piastres
Lesotho	loti	100 lisente
Liberia	Liberian dollar	100 cents
Libya	Libyan dollar	100 cents

World currencies

Nation	Currency unit	Subunits
Liechtenstein	Swiss franc	100 centimes
Lithuania	litas	100 kopecks
Luxembourg	euro	100 cents
Macedonia	denar	100 deni
Madagascar	Malagasy franc	100 centimes
Malawi	kwacha	100 tambala
Malaysia	ringgit	100 sen
Maldives	rufiyaa	100 laari
Mali	CFA franc	100 centimes
Malta	lira	100 cents
Marshall Islands	US dollar	100 cents
Mauritania	ouguiya	5 khoums
Mauritius	rupee	100 cents
Mexico	peso	100 centavos
Moldova	leu	100 bani
Monaco	euro	100 cents
Mongolia	tughrik	100 möngös
Morocco	dirham	100 centimes
Mozambique	metical	100 centavos
Myanmar	kyat	100 pyas
Namibia	South African rand	100 cents
Nauru	Australian dollar	100 cents
Nepal	rupee	100 paisa
Netherlands	euro	100 cents
New Zealand	New Zealand dollar	100 cents

World currencies

Nation	Currency unit	Subunits
Nicaragua	córdoba	100 centavos
Niger	CFA franc	100 centimes
Nigeria	naira	100 kobo
Norway	krone	100 øre
Oman	rial	1000 baiza
Pakistan	rupee	100 paisa
Palau (Belau)	US dollar	100 cents
Panama	balboa	100 centesimos
Papua New Guinea	kina	100 toea
Paraguay	guarani	100 céntimos
Peru	neuvo sol	100 centavos
Philippines	peso	100 centavos
Poland	zloty	100 groszy
Portugal	euro	100 cents
Qatar	riyal	100 dirham
Romania	leu	100 bani
Russia	ruble	100 kopecks
Rwanda	franc	100 centimes
St. Kitts-Nevis	East Caribbean dollar	100 cents
St. Lucia	East Caribbean dollar	100 cents
St. Vincent and the Grenadines	East Caribbean dollar	100 cents
Samoa	tala	100 sene
San Marino	euro	100 cents

World currencies

Nation	Currency unit	Subunits
Sao Tomé and Principe	dobra	100 cêntimos
Saudi Arabia	riyal	100 halalah
Senegal	CFA franc	100 centimes
Seychelles	rupee	100 cents
Sierra Leone	leone	100 cents
Singapore	Singapore dollar	100 cents
Slovakia	koruna	100 haleru
Slovenia	tolar	100 stotins
Solomon Islands	Solomon Islands dollar	100 cents
Somalia	shilling	100 cents
South Africa	rand	100 cents
Spain	euro	100 cents
Sri Lanka	rupee	100 cents
Sudan	pound	100 piastres
Suriname	guilder	100 cents
Swaziland	lilangeni	100 cents
Sweden	krona	100 öre
Switzerland	Swiss franc	100 centimes
Syria	Syrian pound	100 piastres
Taiwan	Taiwan dollar	100 cents
Tajikistan	ruble	100 tanga
Tanzania	shilling	100 cents
Thailand	baht	100 satang
Togo	CFA franc	100 centimes

World currencies

Nation	Currency unit	Subunits
Tonga	pa'anga	100 seniti
Trinidad and Tobago	T & T dollar	100 cents
Tunisia	dinar	1000 millimes
Turkey	lira	100 kurus
Turkmenistan	manat	100 tenesi
Tuvalu	Tuvaluan dollar	100 cents
Uganda	shilling	100 cents
Ukraine	hryvna	100 kopiykas
United Arab Emirates	diram	100 fils
United Kingdom	pound	100 pence
United States	US dollar	100 cents
Uruguay	peso	100 centesimos
Uzbekistan	som	100 tyiyn
Vanuatu	vatu	100 centimes
Vatican City	euro	100 cents
Venezuela	bolivar	100 centimos
Vietnam	dong	10 hao
Yemen	rial	1000 fils
Yugoslavia	dinar	100 paras
Zambia	kwacha	100 ngwee
Zimbabwe	Zimbabwian dollar	100 cents

83. Interest tables

Simple interest on $100:

Days	Annual rate of interest (%)									
	5	6	7	8	9	10	11	12	13	14
1	0.014	0.016	0.019	0.022	0.025	0.027	0.030	0.033	0.036	0.038
2	0.027	0.033	0.038	0.044	0.049	0.055	0.060	0.066	0.071	0.077
3	0.041	0.049	0.058	0.066	0.074	0.082	0.090	0.099	0.107	0.115
4	0.055	0.066	0.077	0.088	0.099	0.110	0.121	0.132	0.142	0.153
5	0.069	0.082	0.096	0.110	0.123	0.137	0.151	0.164	0.178	0.192
6	0.082	0.099	0.115	0.132	0.148	0.164	0.181	0.197	0.214	0.230
7	0.096	0.115	0.134	0.153	0.173	0.192	0.211	0.230	0.249	0.268
8	0.110	0.132	0.153	0.175	0.197	0.219	0.241	0.263	0.285	0.307
9	0.123	0.148	0.173	0.197	0.222	0.247	0.271	0.296	0.321	0.345
10	0.137	0.164	0.192	0.219	0.247	0.274	0.301	0.329	0.356	0.384
20	0.274	0.329	0.384	0.438	0.493	0.548	0.603	0.658	0.712	0.767
30	0.411	0.493	0.575	0.658	0.740	0.822	0.904	0.986	1.07	1.15
40	0.548	0.658	0.767	0.877	0.986	1.10	1.21	1.32	1.42	1.53
50	0.685	0.822	0.959	1.10	1.23	1.37	1.51	1.64	1.78	1.92
60	0.822	0.986	1.15	1.32	1.48	1.64	1.81	1.97	2.14	2.30
70	0.959	1.15	1.34	1.53	1.73	1.92	2.11	2.30	2.49	2.68
8o	1.10	1.32	1.53	1.75	1.97	2.19	2.41	2.63	2.85	3.07
90	1.23	1.48	1.73	1.97	2.22	2.47	2.71	2.96	3.21	3.45
100	1.37	1.64	1.92	2.19	2.17	2.74	3.01	3.29	3.56	3.81
200	2.74	3.29	3.84	4.38	4.93	5.48	6.03	6.58	7.12	7.67
300	4.11	4.93	5.76	6.57	7.10	8.22	9.04	9.87	10.68	11.48

Interest tables

Compound interest on $100 (compounded annually):

Years	Annual rate of interest (%)										
	4	5	6	7	8	9	10	11	12	13	14
1	4	5	6	7	8	9	10	11	12	13	14
2	8	10	12	14	17	19	21	23	25	28	30
3	13	16	19	22	26	30	33	37	40	44	48
4	17	22	26	31	36	41	46	52	57	63	69
5	22	28	34	40	47	54	61	68	76	84	93
6	27	34	42	50	59	68	77	86	97	108	120
7	32	41	50	60	71	83	95	107	121	135	151
8	37	48	59	72	86	99	114	130	147	165	186
9	42	55	69	84	100	117	136	155	177	200	226
10	48	63	79	97	116	137	159	183	210	239	271
11	54	71	90	110	133	158	185	214	247	283	324
12	60	80	101	125	152	181	214	249	289	333	383
13	67	89	113	141	172	207	245	287	335	389	450
14	73	96	126	158	194	234	279	329	387	453	527
15	80	108	140	176	217	264	317	377	446	525	615
20	119	165	221	286	366	460	572	703	863	1051	1277

84. Mortgage Interest Rate Factor Chart

To calculate your monthly principal and interest payments for both fixed and adjustable loans, find the appropriate interest rate, then look at the column for the desired term of the loan (the interest rate factor). To calculate your principal and interest payment, multiply the interest rate factor by the total loan amount in 1,000's.

Factors per $1000

Interest Rate	Term 15 Years	Term 30 Years
4	.7.40	.4.77
4.125	.7.46	.4.85
4.25	.7.52	.4.92
4.375	.7.59	.4.99
4.5	.7.65	.5.07
4.625	.7.71	.5.14
4.75	.7.78	.5.22
4.875	.7.84	.5.29
5	.7.91	.5.37
5.125	.7.97	.5.44
5.25	.8.04	.5.52
5.375	.8.10	.5.60
5.5	.8.17	.5.68
5.625	.8.24	.5.76
5.75	.8.30	.5.84
5.875	.8.37	.5.92
6	.8.44	.6.00

Mortgage Interest Rate Factor Chart

Interest Rate	Term 15 Years	Term 30 Years
6.125	8.51	6.08
6.25	8.57	6.16
6.375	8.64	6.24
6.5	8.71	6.32
6.625	8.78	6.40
6.75	8.85	6.48
6.875	8.92	6.57
7	8.99	6.65
7.125	9.06	6.74
7.25	9.13	6.82
7.375	9.20	6.91
7.5	9.27	6.99
7.625	9.34	7.08
7.75	9.41	7.16
7.875	9.48	7.25
8	9.56	7.34
8.125	9.63	7.42
8.25	9.70	7.51
8.375	9.77	7.60
8.5	9.85	7.69
8.625	9.92	7.78
8.75	9.99	7.87
8.875	10.07	7.96

Mortgage Interest Rate Factor Chart

Interest Rate	Term 15 Years	Term 30 Years
9	10.14	8.05
9.125	10.22	8.14
9.25	10.29	8.23
9.375	10.37	8.32
9.5	10.44	8.41
9.625	10.52	8.50
9.75	10.59	8.59
9.875	10.67	8.68
10	10.75	8.77
10.125	10.82	8.87
10.25	10.90	8.96
10.375	10.98	9.05
10.5	11.05	9.15
10.625	11.13	9.24
10.75	11.21	9.33
10.875	11.29	9.43
11	11.36	9.52
11.125	11.44	9.62
11.25	11.52	9.71
11.375	11.60	9.81
11.5	11.68	9.90
11.625	11.76	10.00
11.75	11.84	10.09
11.875	11.92	10.19

85. Gambling odds

Tossing a coin:

Outcome	Odds against	Probability
Head	1 to 1 (evens)	1/2 = 0.5
Tail	1 to 1 (evens)	1/2 = 0.5

Rolling one dice:

Outcome	Odds against	Probability
1	5 to 1	1/6 = 0.167
2	5 to 1	1/6 = 0.167
3	5 to 1	1/6 = 0.167
4	5 to 1	1/6 = 0.167
5	5 to 1	1/6 = 0.167
6	5 to 1	1/6 = 0.167

Rolling two dice:

Total count	Odds against	Probability
2	35 to 1	1/36 = 0.028
3	17 to 1	2/36 = 1/18 = 0.056
4	11 to 1	3/36 = 1/12 = 0.83
5	8 to 1	4/36 = 1/9 = 0.111
6	31 to 5	5/36 = 0.139
7	5 to 1	6/36 = 1/6 = 0.167
8	31 to 5	5/36 = 0.139
9	8 to 1	4/36 = 1/9 = 0.111
10	11 to 1	3/36 = 1/12 = 0.83
11	17 to 1	2/36 = 1/18 = 0.056
12	35 to 1	1/36 = 0.028

Gambling odds

Poker:

Hand	Possible number	Odds against
royal flush	4	649,739 to 1
straight flush	36	72,192 to 1
four of a kind	624	4164 to 1
full house	3744	693 to 1
flush	5108	508 to 1
straight	10,200	254 to 1
three of a kind	54,912	46 to 1
two pairs	123,552	20 to 1
one pair	1,098,240	1.37 to 1

86. Calendars

Gregorian Calendar:

Month	Number of days
January	31
February	28, or 29 in leap year
March	31
April	30
May	31
June	30
July	31
August	31
September	30
October	31
November	30
December	31

Calendars

Hebrew Calendar:

Month	Number of days	Dates (Gregorian)
Tishri	30	September-October
Heshvan	29 or 30	October-November
Kislev	29 or 30	November-December
Tebet	29	December-January
Shebat	30	January-February
Adar	29 or 30	February-March
Nisan	29	March-April
Iyar	30	April-May
Sivan	30	May-June
Tammuz	29	June-July
Av	30	July-August
Elul	29	August-September

Calendars

Islamic Calendar:

Month	Number of days
Muharram	30
Safar	29
Rabi I	30
Rabi II	29
Jumada I	30
Jumada II	29
Rajab	30
Shaban	29
Ramadan	30
Shawwal	29
Dhu al-Qadah	30
Dhu al-Hijjah	29 or 30 in leap year

Calendars

Month	Number of days	Dates (Gregorian)
Chait'r	29 or 30	March-April
Vaishaakh	29 or 30	April-May
Jayshyth	29 or 30	May-June
Asshaadh	29 or 30	June-July
Shraawan	29 or 30	July-August
Bhaadrap'd	29 or 30	August-September
Aashwin	29 or 30	September-October
Kaartik	29 or 30	October-November
Agarahayana	29 or 30	November-December
Paush	29 or 30	December-January
Maagh	29 or 30	January-February
Phaalgun	29 or 30	February-March

Calendars

Chinese Calendar:

Chinese solar name	Meaning	Date (Gregorian)
Li Chun	spring begins	4/5 February
Yu Shui	rain water	19/20 February
Jing Zhe	insects waken	5/6 March
Chun Fen	vernal equinox	20/21 March
Qing Ming	clear and bright	4/5 April
Gu Yu	grain rains	20/21 April
Li Xia	summer begins	5/6 May
Xiao Man	grain fills	20/21 May
Mang Zhong	grain in ear	5/6 June
Xia Zhi	summer solstice	21/22 June
Xiao Shu	slight heat	6/7 July
Da Shu	great heat	22/23 July
Li Qui	autumn begins	7/8 August
Chu Shu	heat ends	23/24 August
Bai Lu	white dew	7/8 September
Qui Fen	autumn equinox	23/24 September
Han Lu	cold dew	8/9 October
Shuang Jiang	frost descends	23/24 October
Li Dong	winter begins	7/8 November
Kiao Xue	little snow	22/23 November
Da Xue	heavy snow	7/8 December
Dong Zhi	winter solstice	22/23 December
Xiao Han	little cold	5/6 January
Da Han	severe cold	20/21 January

87. Signs of the Zodiac

Name	Dates	Symbol
Aries	March 21 – April 19	Ram
Taurus	April 20 – May 20	Bull
Gemini	May 21 – June 21	Twins
Cancer	June 22 – July 22	Crab
Leo	July 23 – August 22	Lion
Virgo	August 23 – September 22	Virgin
Libra	September 23 – October 22	Scales
Scorpio	October 23 – November 21	Scorpion
Sagittarius	November 22 – December 21	Archer
Capricorn	December 22 – January 19	Goat
Aquarius	January 20 – February 18	Water Bearer
Pisces	February 19 – March 20	Fish

88. US holidays

Name	Date
New Years Day	1 January
Epiphany	Sunday on or before 6 January
Robert E. Lee's Birthday	19 January or 3rd Monday
Martin Luther King Jr. Birthday	3rd Monday in January
National Freedom Day	1 February
Groundhog Day	2 February
Lincoln's Birthday	12 February
Valentine's Day	14 February
Washington's Birthday	22 February
Presidents' Day	3rd Monday in February
Ash Wednesday	47 days before Easter
St Patrick's Day	17 March
Palm Sunday	Sunday before Easter
Good Friday	Friday before Easter
Easter	1st Sunday after 1st full moon after 21 March
Pan American Day	14 April
Arbor Day	Last Friday in April
Ascension	40 days after Easter

US holidays

Name	Date
Pentecost	50 days after Easter
Mother's Day	2nd Sunday in May
Armed Forces Day	3rd Saturday in May
Memorial Day	30 May or last Monday in May
Flag Day	14 June
Father's Day	3rd Sunday in June
Independence Day	4 July
Labor Day	1st Monday in September
Grandparent's Day	Sunday after Labor Day
Columbus Day	12 October or 2nd Monday
United Nations Day	24 October
Halloween	31 October
All Saints' Day	1 November
Election Day	1st Tuesday after 1st Monday
Veterans' Day	11 November
Thanksgiving Day	4th Thursday in November
Christmas Eve	24 December
Christmas Day	25 December
New Year's Eve	31 December

89. World holidays

Name	Date	Where celebrated
New Year's Day	1 January	worldwide
Christmas	6 January	Eastern Orthodox Christian communities
Epiphany	6 January	various Christian communities
Adults' Day	15 January	Japan (for people reaching the age of 20 years)
Epiphany	19 January	Eastern Orthodox Christian communities
Australia Day	1st Monday on or after 26 January	Australia
New Year	2nd new moon after 21 January	China
Tet	January/February	Vietnam
Candlemas Day	2 February	various Christian communities
Bairam	70 days following Ramadan	Muslim communities
Mardi Gras	last day before Lent	Latin America
Shrove Tuesday	last day before Lent	Christian communities
Ash Wednesday	40 days before Easter	various Christian communities
Vernal Equinox Day	21/22 March	Japan

World holidays

Name	Date	Where celebrated
Feast of the Annunciation	25 March	various Christian communities (Lady Day)
Palm Sunday	Sunday before Easter	Christian communities
Good Friday	Friday before Easter	Christian communities
Easter	1st Sunday after 1st full moon after 21 March	Christian communities
Pesach	March/April	Jewish communities
Ramandan	March/April	Muslim communities
All Fools' Day	1 April	various countries
World Health Day	7 April	worldwide
Flower Festival	8 April	Buddhist communities
ANZAC Day	25 April	Australia and New Zealand
Walpurgisnacht	May Day Eve	Germany
May Day	1 May	various countries
Cinco de Mayo	5 May	Mexico
V-E Day	8/9 May	various European countries
African Freedom Day	25 May	various African countries
St John's Eve	23 June	Portugal
Bastille Day	14 July	France
Feast of Lanterns	July	Japan
Muharram	July/August	Muslim communities

World holidays

Name	Date	Where celebrated
Bon Festival	mid-July/mid-August	Buddhist communities
Hiroshima Day	6 August	Japan
Labor Day	1st Monday in September	Canada and the USA
Rosh Hashanah	late September/ early October	Jewish communities
Yom Kippur	September/October	Jewish communities
Halloween	31 October	Christian communities
All Saints' Day	1 November	Christian communities
Remembrance Day	11 November	allied nations of World War I
Labor Thanksgiving Day	23 November	Japan
Saint Nicholas' Day	6 December	The Netherlands
Feast of Lights (Hanukkah)	December	Jewish communities
Christmas Eve	24 December	Christian communities
Christmas Day	25 December	Christian communities
Boxing Day	26 December	various countries
St Stephen's Day	26 December	various European countries
New Year's Eve	31 December	worldwide
Fasching	31 December to Ash Wednesday	Austria and Germany

World holidays

In addition, most countries have a holiday on their National Day, alternatively called Freedom Day, Independence Day, Liberation Day (or something else):

Name	Date	Where celebrated
Afghanistan	19 August	Independence Day
Albania	11 January	Proclamation of the Republic Day
Algeria	3 July	Independence Day
Angola	11 November	Independence Day
Antigua and Barbuda	1 November	National Day
Argentina	25 May	National Day
Australia	26 January or 1st Monday after	Australia Day
Austria	26 October	National Day
Bahamas	10 July	National Day
Bahrain	16 December	Independence Day
Bangladesh	26 March	Independence Day
Barbados	30 November	Independence Day
Belgium	21 July	National Day
Belize	21 September	Independence Day
Benin	1 August	National Day
Bhutan	17 December	National Day
Bolivia	6 August	Independence Day
Botswana	31 Sept-1 Oct.	Independence Days
Brazil	7 September	Independence Day

World holidays

Name	Date	Where celebrated
Brunei	23 February	Independence Day
Bulgaria	3 March	Liberation Day
Burkina Faso	3 January	Revolution Day
Burundi	1 July	Independence Day
Cameroon	20 May	National Day
Canada	1 July	Canada (or Dominion) Day
Cape Verde	5 July	Independence Day
Central African Rep.	13 August	Proclamation of Independence Day
Chad	11 August	Independence Day
Chile	18 September	Independence Day
China	1-2 October	National Days
Colombia	20 July	Independence Day
Comoros	6 July	Independence Day
Congo, Dem. Rep. of	30 June	Independence Day
Congo, Rep. of	13-15 August	Three Glorious Days
Costa Rica	15 September	Independence Day
Cote d'Ivoire	7 December	Independence Day
Cuba	1 January	Liberation Day
Denmark	5 June	Constitution Day
Djibouti	27 June	Independence Day
Dominica	2-3 November	Independence Days
Dominican Republic	27 February	Independence Day

World holidays

Name	Date	Where celebrated
Ecuador	10 August	Independence Day
Egypt	23 July	Anniversary of the Revolution
El Salvador	15 September	Independence Day
Equatorial Guinea	12 October	Independence Day
Estonia	24 February	Independence Day
Ethiopia	12 September	National Revolution Day
Fiji	10 October	Independence Day
Finland	6 December	Independence Day
France	14 July	Bastille Day
Gabon	16-18 August	Independence Anniversary
Gambia	18 February	Independence Day
Germany	3 October	Day of German Unity
Ghana	6 March	Independence Day
Greece	25 March	Independence Day
Grenada	7 February	Independence Day
Guatemala	15 September	Independence Day
Guinea	3 April	Independence Day
Guinea-Bissau	24 September	Independence Day
Guyana	23 February	Republic Day
Haiti	1/2 January	Independence Day
Honduras	15 September	Independence Day

World holidays

Name	Date	Where celebrated
Hungary	15 March	National Day
Iceland	17 June	Anniversary of the Proclamation of the Republic
India	15 August	Independence Day
Indonesia	17 August	Independence Day
Iran	11 February	Revolution Day
Iraq	14 July	Revolution Day
Italy	2 June	Anniversary of the Republic
Jamaica	1st Monday in August	Independence Day
Japan	11 February	National Foundation Day
Jordan	25 May	Independence Day
Kenya	12 December	Independence Day
Kiribati	12 July	Independence Day
Korea, North	9 September	Independence Day
Korea, South	1 March	Independence Day
Kuwait	25 February	National Day
Laos	2 December	National Day
Latvia	18 November	Independence Day
Lebanon	22 November	Independence Day
Lesotho	4 October	Independence Day
Liberia	26 July	Independence Day

World holidays

Name	Date	Where celebrated
Libya	1 September	National (or Revolution) Day
Lithuania	16 February	Independence Day
Luxembourg	23 June	National Day
Madagascar	26 June	Independence Day
Malawi	6 July	Independence Day
Malaysia	31 August	Merdeka (National) Day
Maldives	26/27 July	Independence Day
Mali	22 September	Anniversary of the Proclamation of the Republic
Malta	21 September	Independence Day
Marshall Islands	21 October	Independence Day
Mauritania	28 November	Independence Day
Mauritius	12 March	Independence Day
Mexico	16 September	Independence Day
Mongolia	11-12 July	National Days
Morocco	3 March	National Day
Mozambique	25 June	Independence Day
Myanmar	4 January	Independence Day
Namibia	21 March	Independence Day
Nauru	31 January	Independence Day
New Zealand	6 February	Waitangi (or New Zealand) Day

World holidays

Name	Date	Where celebrated
Nicaragua	15 September	Independence Day
Niger	3 August	Independence Day
Nigeria	1 October	Independence Day
Oman	18-20 Nov.	National Days
Pakistan	14 August	Independence Day
Panama	3 November	Independence Day
Papua New Guinea	16 September	Independence Day
Paraguay	14/15 May	Independence Day
Peru	28-29 July	Independence Days
Philippine	12 June	Independence Day
Poland	11 November	Independence Day
Portugal	10 June	Portugal's Day
Puerto Rico	25 July	Commonwealth Day
Qatar	3 September	Independence Day
Romania	1 December	National Day
Rwanda	1 July	Independence Day
St. Kitts-Nevis	19 September	Independence Day
St. Lucia	22 February	Independence Day
St. Vincent and the Grenadines	27 October	Thanksgiving and Independence Day
Samoa	1-3 June	Independence Days
Sao Tomé and Principe	12 July	Anniversary of National Independence

World holidays

Name	Date	Where celebrated
Saudi Arabia	12 September	National Day
Senegal	4 April	National Day
Seychelles	29 June	Independence Day
Sierra Leone	27 April	Independence Day
Singapore	16 September	Independence Day
Solomon Islands	7 July	Independence Day
Somalia	26 June	Independence Day
South Africa	31 May	Republic Day
Sri Lanka	4 February	Independence and National Day
Sudan	1 January	Independence Day
Suriname	25 November	Independence Day
Swaziland	6 September	Sobhuza Day
Sweden	6 June	National Day
Switzerland	1 August	Anniversary of the Founding of the Swiss Confederation
Syria	17 April	Independence Day
Taiwan	25 December	Constitution Day
Tanzania	9 December	Independence and Republic Day
Thailand	6 April	Chakri Day
Togo	13 January	Liberation Day
Tonga	4 June	Emancipation Day
Trinidad and Tobago	31 August	Independence Day

World holidays

Name	Date	Where celebrated
Tunisia	20 March	Independence Day
Turkey	20 October	Anniversary of the Declaration of the Republic
Tuvalu	1-2 October	Tuvalu Days
Uganda	9 October	Independence Day
United Arab Emirates	2 December	National Day
United States	4 July	Independence Day
Uruguay	25 August	Independence Day
Vanuatu	30 July	Independence Day
Vatican City	11 February	Independence Anniversary
Venezuela	5 July	Independence Day
Vietnam	2-3 September	Independence Days
Yemen	26 September	National Day
Zambia	24 October	Independence Day
Zimbabwe	18 April	Independence Day

90. Perpetual calendar

There are 14 possible different calendars, which change from year to year. To find the calendar for any year between 1925 and 2025, look up its code letter in the following table. Then find the calendar with that code letter in the pages that follow.

Year	Code letter	Year	Code letter	Year	Code letter	Year	Code letter
1925	A	1939	H	1953	A	1967	H
1926	B	1940	K	1954	B	1968	K
1927	C	1941	F	1955	C	1969	F
1928	D	1942	A	1956	D	1970	A
1929	E	1943	B	1957	E	1971	B
1930	F	1944	L	1958	F	1972	L
1931	A	1945	I	1959	A	1973	I
1932	G	1946	E	1960	G	1974	E
1933	H	1947	F	1961	H	1975	F
1934	I	1948	M	1962	I	1976	M
1935	E	1949	A	1963	E	1977	C
1936	J	1950	B	1964	J	1978	H
1937	B	1951	I	1965	B	1979	I
1938	C	1952	N	1966	C	1980	N

Perpetual calendar

Year	Code letter	Year	Code letter	Year	Code letter	Year	Code letter
1981	A	1993	B	2005	C	2017	H
1982	B	1994	C	2006	H	2018	I
1983	C	1995	H	2007	I	2019	E
1984	D	1996	K	2008	N	2020	J
1985	E	1997	F	2009	A	2021	B
1986	F	1998	A	2010	B	2022	C
1987	A	1999	B	2011	C	2023	H
1988	G	2000	L	2012	D	2024	K
1989	H	2001	I	2013	E	2025	F
1990	I	2002	E	2014	F		
1991	E	2003	F	2015	A		
1992	J	2004	M	2016	G		

Calendar A

January

S	M	T	W	T	F	S
				1	2	3
4	5	6	7	8	9	10
11	12	13	14	15	16	17
18	19	20	21	22	23	24
25	26	27	28	29	30	31

February

S	M	T	W	T	F	S
1	2	3	4	5	6	7
8	9	10	11	12	13	14
15	16	17	18	19	20	21
22	23	24	25	26	27	28

March

S	M	T	W	T	F	S
1	2	3	4	5	6	7
8	9	10	11	12	13	14
15	16	17	18	19	20	21
22	23	24	25	26	27	28
29	30	31				

Calendar A

April

S	M	T	W	T	F	S
			1	2	3	4
5	6	7	8	9	10	11
12	13	14	15	16	17	18
19	20	21	22	23	24	25
26	27	28	29	30		

May

S	M	T	W	T	F	S
					1	2
3	4	5	6	7	8	9
10	11	12	13	14	15	16
17	18	19	20	21	22	23
24	25	26	27	28	29	30
31						

June

S	M	T	W	T	F	S
	1	2	3	4	5	6
7	8	9	10	11	12	13
14	15	16	17	18	19	20
21	22	23	24	25	26	27
28	29	30				

Calendar A

July

S	M	T	W	T	F	S
			1	2	3	4
5	6	7	8	9	10	11
12	13	14	15	16	17	18
19	20	21	22	23	24	25
26	27	28	29	30	31	

August

S	M	T	W	T	F	S
						1
2	3	4	5	6	7	8
9	10	11	12	13	14	15
16	17	18	19	20	21	22
23	24	25	26	27	28	29
30	31					

September

S	M	T	W	T	F	S
		1	2	3	4	5
6	7	8	9	10	11	12
13	14	15	16	17	18	19
20	21	22	23	24	25	26
27	28	29	30			

Calendar A

October

S	M	T	W	T	F	S
				1	2	3
4	5	6	7	8	9	10
11	12	13	14	15	16	17
18	19	20	21	22	23	24
25	26	27	28	29	30	31

November

S	M	T	W	T	F	S
1	2	3	4	5	6	7
8	9	10	11	12	13	14
15	16	17	18	19	20	21
22	23	24	25	26	27	28
29	30					

December

S	M	T	W	T	F	S
		1	2	3	4	5
6	7	8	9	10	11	12
13	14	15	16	17	18	19
20	21	22	23	24	25	26
27	28	29	30	31		

Calendar B

January

S	M	T	W	T	F	S
					1	2
3	4	5	6	7	8	9
10	11	12	13	14	15	16
17	18	19	20	21	22	23
24	25	26	27	28	29	30
31						

February

S	M	T	W	T	F	S
	1	2	3	4	5	6
7	8	9	10	11	12	13
14	15	16	17	18	19	20
21	22	23	24	25	26	27
28						

March

S	M	T	W	T	F	S
	1	2	3	4	5	6
7	8	9	10	11	12	13
14	15	16	17	18	19	20
21	22	23	24	25	26	27
28	29	30	31			

Calendar B

April

S	M	T	W	T	F	S
				1	2	3
4	5	6	7	8	9	10
11	12	13	14	15	16	17
18	19	20	21	22	23	24
25	26	27	28	29	30	

May

S	M	T	W	T	F	S
						1
2	3	4	5	6	7	8
9	10	11	12	13	14	15
16	17	18	19	20	21	22
23	24	25	26	27	28	29
30	31					

June

S	M	T	W	T	F	S
		1	2	3	4	5
6	7	8	9	10	11	12
13	14	15	16	17	18	19
20	21	22	23	24	25	26
27	28	29	30			

Calendar B

July

S	M	T	W	T	F	S
				1	2	3
4	5	6	7	8	9	10
11	12	13	14	15	16	17
18	19	20	21	22	23	24
25	26	27	28	29	30	31

August

S	M	T	W	T	F	S
1	2	3	4	5	6	7
8	9	10	11	12	13	14
15	16	17	18	19	20	21
22	23	24	25	26	27	28
29	30	31				

September

S	M	T	W	T	F	S
			1	2	3	4
5	6	7	8	9	10	11
12	13	14	15	16	17	18
19	20	21	22	23	24	25
26	27	28	29	30		

Calendar B

October

S	M	T	W	T	F	S
					1	2
3	4	5	6	7	8	9
10	11	12	13	14	15	16
17	18	19	20	21	22	23
24	25	26	27	28	29	30
31						

November

S	M	T	W	T	F	S
	1	2	3	4	5	6
7	8	9	10	11	12	13
14	15	16	17	18	19	20
21	22	23	24	25	26	27
28	29	30				

December

S	M	T	W	T	F	S
			1	2	3	4
5	6	7	8	9	10	11
12	13	14	15	16	17	18
19	20	21	22	23	24	25
26	27	28	29	30	31	

Calendar C

January

S	M	T	W	T	F	S
						1
2	3	4	5	6	7	8
9	10	11	12	13	14	15
16	17	18	19	20	21	22
23	24	25	26	27	28	29
30	31					

February

S	M	T	W	T	F	S
		1	2	3	4	5
6	7	8	9	10	11	12
13	14	15	16	17	18	19
20	21	22	23	24	25	26
27	28					

March

S	M	T	W	T	F	S
		1	2	3	4	5
6	7	8	9	10	11	12
13	14	15	16	17	18	19
20	21	22	23	24	25	26
27	28	29	30	31		

Calendar C

April

S	M	T	W	T	F	S
					1	2
3	4	5	6	7	8	9
10	11	12	13	14	15	16
17	18	19	20	21	22	23
24	25	26	27	28	29	30

May

S	M	T	W	T	F	S
1	2	3	4	5	6	7
8	9	10	11	12	13	14
15	16	17	18	19	20	21
22	23	24	25	26	27	28
29	30	31				

June

S	M	T	W	T	F	S
			1	2	3	4
5	6	7	8	9	10	11
12	13	14	15	16	17	18
19	20	21	22	23	24	25
26	27	28	29	30		

Calendar C

July

S	M	T	W	T	F	S
					1	2
3	4	5	6	7	8	9
10	11	12	13	14	15	16
17	18	19	20	21	22	23
24	25	26	27	28	29	30
31						

August

S	M	T	W	T	F	S
	1	2	3	4	5	6
7	8	9	10	11	12	13
14	15	16	17	18	19	20
21	22	23	24	25	26	27
28	29	30	31			

September

S	M	T	W	T	F	S
				1	2	3
4	5	6	7	8	9	10
11	12	13	14	15	16	17
18	19	20	21	22	23	24
25	26	27	28	29	30	

Calendar C

October

S	M	T	W	T	F	S
						1
2	3	4	5	6	7	8
9	10	11	12	13	14	15
16	17	18	19	20	21	22
23	24	25	26	27	28	29
30	31					

November

S	M	T	W	T	F	S
		1	2	3	4	5
6	7	8	9	10	11	12
13	14	15	16	17	18	19
20	21	22	23	24	25	26
27	28	29	30			

December

S	M	T	W	T	F	S
				1	2	3
4	5	6	7	8	9	10
11	12	13	14	15	16	17
18	19	20	21	22	23	24
25	26	27	28	29	30	31

Calendar D

January

S	M	T	W	T	F	S
1	2	3	4	5	6	7
8	9	10	11	12	13	14
15	16	17	18	19	20	21
22	23	24	25	26	27	28
29	30	31				

February

S	M	T	W	T	F	S
			1	2	3	4
5	6	7	8	9	10	11
12	13	14	15	16	17	18
19	20	21	22	23	24	25
26	27	28	29			

March

S	M	T	W	T	F	S
				1	2	3
4	5	6	7	8	9	10
11	12	13	14	15	16	17
18	19	20	21	22	23	24
25	26	27	28	29	30	31

Calendar D

April

S	M	T	W	T	F	S
1	2	3	4	5	6	7
8	9	10	11	12	13	14
15	16	17	18	19	20	21
22	23	24	25	26	27	28
29	30					

May

S	M	T	W	T	F	S
		1	2	3	4	5
6	7	8	9	10	11	12
13	14	15	16	17	18	19
20	21	22	23	24	25	26
27	28	29	30	31		

June

S	M	T	W	T	F	S
					1	2
3	4	5	6	7	8	9
10	11	12	13	14	15	16
17	18	19	20	21	22	23
24	25	26	27	28	29	30

Calendar D

July

S	M	T	W	T	F	S
1	2	3	4	5	6	7
8	9	10	11	12	13	14
15	16	17	18	19	20	21
22	23	24	25	26	27	28
29	30	31				

August

S	M	T	W	T	F	S
			1	2	3	4
5	6	7	8	9	10	11
12	13	14	15	16	17	18
19	20	21	22	23	24	25
26	27	28	29	30	31	

September

S	M	T	W	T	F	S
						1
2	3	4	5	6	7	8
9	10	11	12	13	14	15
16	17	18	19	20	21	22
23	24	25	26	27	28	29
30						

Calendar D

October

S	M	T	W	T	F	S
	1	2	3	4	5	6
7	8	9	10	11	12	13
14	15	16	17	18	19	20
21	22	23	24	25	26	27
28	29	30	31			

November

S	M	T	W	T	F	S
				1	2	3
4	5	6	7	8	9	10
11	12	13	14	15	16	17
18	19	20	21	22	23	24
25	26	27	28	29	30	

December

S	M	T	W	T	F	S
						1
2	3	4	5	6	7	8
9	10	11	12	13	14	15
16	17	18	19	20	21	22
23	24	25	26	27	28	29
30	31					

Calendar E

January

S	M	T	W	T	F	S
		1	2	3	4	5
6	7	8	9	10	11	12
13	14	15	16	17	18	19
20	21	22	23	24	25	26
27	28	29	30	31		

February

S	M	T	W	T	F	S
					1	2
3	4	5	6	7	8	9
10	11	12	13	14	15	16
17	18	19	20	21	22	23
24	25	26	27	28		

March

S	M	T	W	T	F	S
					1	2
3	4	5	6	7	8	9
10	11	12	13	14	15	16
17	18	19	20	21	22	23
24	25	26	27	28	29	30
31						

Calendar E

April

S	M	T	W	T	F	S
	1	2	3	4	5	6
7	8	9	10	11	12	13
14	15	16	17	18	19	20
21	22	23	24	25	26	27
28	29	30				

May

S	M	T	W	T	F	S
			1	2	3	4
5	6	7	8	9	10	11
12	13	14	15	16	17	18
19	20	21	22	23	24	25
26	27	28	29	30	31	

June

S	M	T	W	T	F	S
						1
2	3	4	5	6	7	8
9	10	11	12	13	14	15
16	17	18	19	20	21	22
23	24	25	26	27	28	29
30						

Calendar E

July

S	M	T	W	T	F	S
	1	2	3	4	5	6
7	8	9	10	11	12	13
14	15	16	17	18	19	20
21	22	23	24	25	26	27
28	29	30	31			

August

S	M	T	W	T	F	S
				1	2	3
4	5	6	7	8	9	10
11	12	13	14	15	16	17
18	19	20	21	22	23	24
25	26	27	28	29	30	31

September

S	M	T	W	T	F	S
1	2	3	4	5	6	7
8	9	10	11	12	13	14
15	16	17	18	19	20	21
22	23	24	25	26	27	28
29	30					

Calendar E

October

S	M	T	W	T	F	S
		1	2	3	4	5
6	7	8	9	10	11	12
13	14	15	16	17	18	19
20	21	22	23	24	25	26
27	28	29	30	31		

November

S	M	T	W	T	F	S
					1	2
3	4	5	6	7	8	9
10	11	12	13	14	15	16
17	18	19	20	21	22	23
24	25	26	27	28	29	30

December

S	M	T	W	T	F	S
1	2	3	4	5	6	7
8	9	10	11	12	13	14
15	16	17	18	19	20	21
22	23	24	25	26	27	28
29	30	31				

Calendar F

January

S	M	T	W	T	F	S
			1	2	3	4
5	6	7	8	9	10	11
12	13	14	15	16	17	18
19	20	21	22	23	24	25
26	27	28	29	30	31	

February

S	M	T	W	T	F	S
						1
2	3	4	5	6	7	8
9	10	11	12	13	14	15
16	17	18	19	20	21	22
23	24	25	26	27	28	

March

S	M	T	W	T	F	S
						1
2	3	4	5	6	7	8
9	10	11	12	13	14	15
16	17	18	19	20	21	22
23	24	25	26	27	28	29
30	31					

Calendar F

April

S	M	T	W	T	F	S
		1	2	3	4	5
6	7	8	9	10	11	12
13	14	15	16	17	18	19
20	21	22	23	24	25	26
27	28	29	30			

May

S	M	T	W	T	F	S
				1	2	3
4	5	6	7	8	9	10
11	12	13	14	15	16	17
18	19	20	21	22	23	24
25	26	27	28	29	30	31

June

S	M	T	W	T	F	S
1	2	3	4	5	6	7
8	9	10	11	12	13	14
15	16	17	18	19	20	21
22	23	24	25	26	27	28
29	30					

Calendar F

July

S	M	T	W	T	F	S
		1	2	3	4	5
6	7	8	9	10	11	12
13	14	15	16	17	18	19
20	21	22	23	24	25	26
27	28	29	30	31		

August

S	M	T	W	T	F	S
					1	2
3	4	5	6	7	8	9
10	11	12	13	14	15	16
17	18	19	20	21	22	23
24	25	26	27	28	29	30
31						

September

S	M	T	W	T	F	S
	1	2	3	4	5	6
7	8	9	10	11	12	13
14	15	16	17	18	19	20
21	22	23	24	25	26	27
28	29	30				

Calendar F

October

S	M	T	W	T	F	S
			1	2	3	4
5	6	7	8	9	10	11
12	13	14	15	16	17	18
19	20	21	22	23	24	25
26	27	28	29	30	31	

November

S	M	T	W	T	F	S
						1
2	3	4	5	6	7	8
9	10	11	12	13	14	15
16	17	18	19	20	21	22
23	24	25	26	27	28	29
30						

December

S	M	T	W	T	F	S
	1	2	3	4	5	6
7	8	9	10	11	12	13
14	15	16	17	18	19	20
21	22	23	24	25	26	27
28	29	30	31			

Calendar G

January

S	M	T	W	T	F	S
					1	2
3	4	5	6	7	8	9
10	11	12	13	14	15	16
17	18	19	20	21	22	23
24	25	26	27	28	29	30
31						

February

S	M	T	W	T	F	S
	1	2	3	4	5	6
7	8	9	10	11	12	13
14	15	16	17	18	19	20
21	22	23	24	25	26	27
28	29					

March

S	M	T	W	T	F	S
		1	2	3	4	5
6	7	8	9	10	11	12
13	14	15	16	17	18	19
20	21	22	23	24	25	26
27	28	29	30	31		

Calendar G

April

S	M	T	W	T	F	S
					1	2
3	4	5	6	7	8	9
10	11	12	13	14	15	16
17	18	19	20	21	22	23
24	25	26	27	28	29	30

May

S	M	T	W	T	F	S
1	2	3	4	5	6	7
8	9	10	11	12	13	14
15	16	17	18	19	20	21
22	23	24	25	26	27	28
29	30	31				

June

S	M	T	W	T	F	S
			1	2	3	4
5	6	7	8	9	10	11
12	13	14	15	16	17	18
19	20	21	22	23	24	25
26	27	28	29	30		

Calendar G

July

S	M	T	W	T	F	S
					1	2
3	4	5	6	7	8	9
10	11	12	13	14	15	16
17	18	19	20	21	22	23
24	25	26	27	28	29	30
31						

August

S	M	T	W	T	F	S
	1	2	3	4	5	6
7	8	9	10	11	12	13
14	15	16	17	18	19	20
21	22	23	24	25	26	27
28	29	30	31			

September

S	M	T	W	T	F	S
				1	2	3
4	5	6	7	8	9	10
11	12	13	14	15	16	17
18	19	20	21	22	23	24
25	26	27	28	29	30	

Calendar G

October

S	M	T	W	T	F	S
						1
2	3	4	5	6	7	8
9	10	11	12	13	14	15
16	17	18	19	20	21	22
23	24	25	26	27	28	29
30	31					

November

S	M	T	W	T	F	S
		1	2	3	4	5
6	7	8	9	10	11	12
13	14	15	16	17	18	19
20	21	22	23	24	25	26
27	28	29	30			

December

S	M	T	W	T	F	S
				1	2	3
4	5	6	7	8	9	10
11	12	13	14	15	16	17
18	19	20	21	22	23	24
25	26	27	28	29	30	31

Calendar H

January

S	M	T	W	T	F	S
1	2	3	4	5	6	7
8	9	10	11	12	13	14
15	16	17	18	19	20	21
22	23	24	25	26	27	28
29	30	31				

February

S	M	T	W	T	F	S
			1	2	3	4
5	6	7	8	9	10	11
12	13	14	15	16	17	18
19	20	21	22	23	24	25
26	27	28				

March

S	M	T	W	T	F	S
			1	2	3	4
5	6	7	8	9	10	11
12	13	14	15	16	17	18
19	20	21	22	23	24	25
26	27	28	29	30	31	

Calendar H

April

S	M	T	W	T	F	S
						1
2	3	4	5	6	7	8
9	10	11	12	13	14	15
16	17	18	19	20	21	22
23	24	25	26	27	28	29
30						

May

S	M	T	W	T	F	S
	1	2	3	4	5	6
7	8	9	10	11	12	13
14	15	16	17	18	19	20
21	22	23	24	25	26	27
28	29	30	31			

June

S	M	T	W	T	F	S
				1	2	3
4	5	6	7	8	9	10
11	12	13	14	15	16	17
18	19	20	21	22	23	24
25	26	27	28	29	30	

Calendar H

July

S	M	T	W	T	F	S
						1
2	3	4	5	6	7	8
9	10	11	12	13	14	15
16	17	18	19	20	21	22
23	24	25	26	27	28	29
30	31					

August

S	M	T	W	T	F	S
		1	2	3	4	5
6	7	8	9	10	11	12
13	14	15	16	17	18	19
20	21	22	23	24	25	26
27	28	29	30	31		

September

S	M	T	W	T	F	S
					1	2
3	4	5	6	7	8	9
10	11	12	13	14	15	16
17	18	19	20	21	22	23
24	25	26	27	28	29	30

Calendar H

October

S	M	T	W	T	F	S
1	2	3	4	5	6	7
8	9	10	11	12	13	14
15	16	17	18	19	20	21
22	23	24	25	26	27	28
29	30	31				

November

S	M	T	W	T	F	S
			1	2	3	4
5	6	7	8	9	10	11
12	13	14	15	16	17	18
19	20	21	22	23	24	25
26	27	28	29	30		

December

S	M	T	W	T	F	S
					1	2
3	4	5	6	7	8	9
10	11	12	13	14	15	16
17	18	19	20	21	22	23
24	25	26	27	28	29	30
31						

Calendar I

January

S	M	T	W	T	F	S
	1	2	3	4	5	6
7	8	9	10	11	12	13
14	15	16	17	18	19	20
21	22	23	24	25	26	27
28	29	30	31			

February

S	M	T	W	T	F	S
				1	2	3
4	5	6	7	8	9	10
11	12	13	14	15	16	17
18	19	20	21	22	23	24
25	26	27	28			

March

S	M	T	W	T	F	S
				1	2	3
4	5	6	7	8	9	10
11	12	13	14	15	16	17
18	19	20	21	22	23	24
25	26	27	28	29	30	31

Calendar I

April

S	M	T	W	T	F	S
1	2	3	4	5	6	7
8	9	10	11	12	13	14
15	16	17	18	19	20	21
22	23	24	25	26	27	28
29	30					

May

S	M	T	W	T	F	S
		1	2	3	4	5
6	7	8	9	10	11	12
13	14	15	16	17	18	19
20	21	22	23	24	25	26
27	28	29	30	31		

June

S	M	T	W	T	F	S
					1	2
3	4	5	6	7	8	9
10	11	12	13	14	15	16
17	18	19	20	21	22	23
24	25	26	27	28	29	30

Calendar I

July

S	M	T	W	T	F	S
1	2	3	4	5	6	7
8	9	10	11	12	13	14
15	16	17	18	19	20	21
22	23	24	25	26	27	28
29	30	31				

August

S	M	T	W	T	F	S
			1	2	3	4
5	6	7	8	9	10	11
12	13	14	15	16	17	18
19	20	21	22	23	24	25
26	27	28	29	30	31	

September

S	M	T	W	T	F	S
						1
2	3	4	5	6	7	8
9	10	11	12	13	14	15
16	17	18	19	20	21	22
23	24	25	26	27	28	29
30						

Calendar I

October

S	M	T	W	T	F	S
	1	2	3	4	5	6
7	8	9	10	11	12	13
14	15	16	17	18	19	20
21	22	23	24	25	26	27
28	29	30	31			

November

S	M	T	W	T	F	S
				1	2	3
4	5	6	7	8	9	10
11	12	13	14	15	16	17
18	19	20	21	22	23	24
25	26	27	28	29	30	

December

S	M	T	W	T	F	S
						1
2	3	4	5	6	7	8
9	10	11	12	13	14	15
16	17	18	19	20	21	22
23	24	25	26	27	28	29
30	31					

Calendar J

January

S	M	T	W	T	F	S
			1	2	3	4
5	6	7	8	9	10	11
12	13	14	15	16	17	18
19	20	21	22	23	24	25
26	27	28	29	30	31	

February

S	M	T	W	T	F	S
						1
2	3	4	5	6	7	8
9	10	11	12	13	14	15
16	17	18	19	20	21	22
23	24	25	26	27	28	29

March

S	M	T	W	T	F	S
1	2	3	4	5	6	7
8	9	10	11	12	13	14
15	16	17	18	19	20	21
22	23	24	25	26	27	28
29	30	31				

Calendar J

April

S	M	T	W	T	F	S
			1	2	3	4
5	6	7	8	9	10	11
12	13	14	15	16	17	18
19	20	21	22	23	24	25
26	27	28	29	30		

May

S	M	T	W	T	F	S
					1	2
3	4	5	6	7	8	9
10	11	12	13	14	15	16
17	18	19	20	21	22	23
24	25	26	27	28	29	30
31						

June

S	M	T	W	T	F	S
	1	2	3	4	5	6
7	8	9	10	11	12	13
14	15	16	17	18	19	20
21	22	23	24	25	26	27
28	29	30				

Calendar J

July

S	M	T	W	T	F	S
			1	2	3	4
5	6	7	8	9	10	11
12	13	14	15	16	17	18
19	20	21	22	23	24	25
26	27	28	29	30	31	

August

S	M	T	W	T	F	S
						1
2	3	4	5	6	7	8
9	10	11	12	13	14	15
16	17	18	19	20	21	22
23	24	25	26	27	28	29
30	31					

September

S	M	T	W	T	F	S
		1	2	3	4	5
6	7	8	9	10	11	12
13	14	15	16	17	18	19
20	21	22	23	24	25	26
27	28	29	30			

Calendar J

October

S	M	T	W	T	F	S
				1	2	3
4	5	6	7	8	9	10
11	12	13	14	15	16	17
18	19	20	21	22	23	24
25	26	27	28	29	30	31

November

S	M	T	W	T	F	S
1	2	3	4	5	6	7
8	9	10	11	12	13	14
15	16	17	18	19	20	21
22	23	24	25	26	27	28
29	30					

December

S	M	T	W	T	F	S
		1	2	3	4	5
6	7	8	9	10	11	12
13	14	15	16	17	18	19
20	21	22	23	24	25	26
27	28	29	30	31		

Calendar K

January

S	M	T	W	T	F	S
	1	2	3	4	5	6
7	8	9	10	11	12	13
14	15	16	17	18	19	20
21	22	23	24	25	26	27
28	29	30	31			

February

S	M	T	W	T	F	S
				1	2	3
4	5	6	7	8	9	10
11	12	13	14	15	16	17
18	19	20	21	22	23	24
25	26	27	28	29		

March

S	M	T	W	T	F	S
					1	2
3	4	5	6	7	8	9
10	11	12	13	14	15	16
17	18	19	20	21	22	23
24	25	26	27	28	29	30
31						

Calendar K

April

S	M	T	W	T	F	S
	1	2	3	4	5	6
7	8	9	10	11	12	13
14	15	16	17	18	19	20
21	22	23	24	25	26	27
28	29	30				

May

S	M	T	W	T	F	S
			1	2	3	4
5	6	7	8	9	10	11
12	13	14	15	16	17	18
19	20	21	22	23	24	25
26	27	28	29	30	31	

June

S	M	T	W	T	F	S
						1
2	3	4	5	6	7	8
9	10	11	12	13	14	15
16	17	18	19	20	21	22
23	24	25	26	27	28	29
30						

Calendar K

July

S	M	T	W	T	F	S
	1	2	3	4	5	6
7	8	9	10	11	12	13
14	15	16	17	18	19	20
21	22	23	24	25	26	27
28	29	30	31			

August

S	M	T	W	T	F	S
				1	2	3
4	5	6	7	8	9	10
11	12	13	14	15	16	17
18	19	20	21	22	23	24
25	26	27	28	29	30	31

September

S	M	T	W	T	F	S
1	2	3	4	5	6	7
8	9	10	11	12	13	14
15	16	17	18	19	20	21
22	23	24	25	26	27	28
29	30					

Calendar K

October

S	M	T	W	T	F	S
		1	2	3	4	5
6	7	8	9	10	11	12
13	14	15	16	17	18	19
20	21	22	23	24	25	26
27	28	29	30	31		

November

S	M	T	W	T	F	S
					1	2
3	4	5	6	7	8	9
10	11	12	13	14	15	16
17	18	19	20	21	22	23
24	25	26	27	28	29	30

December

S	M	T	W	T	F	S
1	2	3	4	5	6	7
8	9	10	11	12	13	14
15	16	17	18	19	20	21
22	23	24	25	26	27	28
29	30	31				

Calendar L

January

S	M	T	W	T	F	S
						1
2	3	4	5	6	7	8
9	10	11	12	13	14	15
16	17	18	19	20	21	22
23	24	25	26	27	28	29
30	31					

February

S	M	T	W	T	F	S
		1	2	3	4	5
6	7	8	9	10	11	12
13	14	15	16	17	18	19
20	21	22	23	24	25	26
27	28	29				

March

S	M	T	W	T	F	S
			1	2	3	4
5	6	7	8	9	10	11
12	13	14	15	16	17	18
19	20	21	22	23	24	25
26	27	28	29	30	31	

Calendar L

April

S	M	T	W	T	F	S
						1
2	3	4	5	6	7	8
9	10	11	12	13	14	15
16	17	18	19	20	21	22
23	24	25	26	27	28	29
30						

May

S	M	T	W	T	F	S
	1	2	3	4	5	6
7	8	9	10	11	12	13
14	15	16	17	18	19	20
21	22	23	24	25	26	27
28	29	30	31			

June

S	M	T	W	T	F	S
				1	2	3
4	5	6	7	8	9	10
11	12	13	14	15	16	17
18	19	20	21	22	23	24
25	26	27	28	29	30	

Calendar L

July

S	M	T	W	T	F	S
						1
2	3	4	5	6	7	8
9	10	11	12	13	14	15
16	17	18	19	20	21	22
23	24	25	26	27	28	29
30	31					

August

S	M	T	W	T	F	S
		1	2	3	4	5
6	7	8	9	10	11	12
13	14	15	16	17	18	19
20	21	22	23	24	25	26
27	28	29	30	31		

September

S	M	T	W	T	F	S
					1	2
3	4	5	6	7	8	9
10	11	12	13	14	15	16
17	18	19	20	21	22	23
24	25	26	27	28	29	30

Calendar L

October

S	M	T	W	T	F	S
1	2	3	4	5	6	7
8	9	10	11	12	13	14
15	16	17	18	19	20	21
22	23	24	25	26	27	28
29	30	31				

November

S	M	T	W	T	F	S
			1	2	3	4
5	6	7	8	9	10	11
12	13	14	15	16	17	18
19	20	21	22	23	24	25
26	27	28	29	30		

December

S	M	T	W	T	F	S
					1	2
3	4	5	6	7	8	9
10	11	12	13	14	15	16
17	18	19	20	21	22	23
24	25	26	27	28	29	30
31						

Calendar M

January

S	M	T	W	T	F	S
				1	2	3
4	5	6	7	8	9	10
11	12	13	14	15	16	17
18	19	20	21	22	23	24
25	26	27	28	29	30	31

February

S	M	T	W	T	F	S
1	2	3	4	5	6	7
8	9	10	11	12	13	14
15	16	17	18	19	20	21
22	23	24	25	26	27	28
29						

March

S	M	T	W	T	F	S
	1	2	3	4	5	6
7	8	9	10	11	12	13
14	15	16	17	18	19	20
21	22	23	24	25	26	27
28	29	30	31			

Calendar M

April

S	M	T	W	T	F	S
				1	2	3
4	5	6	7	8	9	10
11	12	13	14	15	16	17
18	19	20	21	22	23	24
25	26	27	28	29	30	

May

S	M	T	W	T	F	S
						1
2	3	4	5	6	7	8
9	10	11	12	13	14	15
16	17	18	19	20	21	22
23	24	25	26	27	28	29
30	31					

June

S	M	T	W	T	F	S
		1	2	3	4	5
6	7	8	9	10	11	12
13	14	15	16	17	18	19
20	21	22	23	24	25	26
27	28	29	30			

Calendar M

July

S	M	T	W	T	F	S
				1	2	3
4	5	6	7	8	9	10
11	12	13	14	15	16	17
18	19	20	21	22	23	24
25	26	27	28	29	30	31

August

S	M	T	W	T	F	S
1	2	3	4	5	6	7
8	9	10	11	12	13	14
15	16	17	18	19	20	21
22	23	24	25	26	27	28
29	30	31				

September

S	M	T	W	T	F	S
			1	2	3	4
5	6	7	8	9	10	11
12	13	14	15	16	17	18
19	20	21	22	23	24	25
26	27	28	29	30		

Calendar M

October

S	M	T	W	T	F	S
					1	2
3	4	5	6	7	8	9
10	11	12	13	14	15	16
17	18	19	20	21	22	23
24	25	26	27	28	29	30
31						

November

S	M	T	W	T	F	S
	1	2	3	4	5	6
7	8	9	10	11	12	13
14	15	16	17	18	19	20
21	22	23	24	25	26	27
28	29	30				

December

S	M	T	W	T	F	S
			1	2	3	4
5	6	7	8	9	10	11
12	13	14	15	16	17	18
19	20	21	22	23	24	25
26	27	28	29	3	31	

Calendar N

January

S	M	T	W	T	F	S
		1	2	3	4	5
6	7	8	9	10	11	12
13	14	15	16	17	18	19
20	21	22	23	24	25	26
27	28	29	30	31		

February

S	M	T	W	T	F	S
					1	2
3	4	5	6	7	8	9
10	11	12	13	14	15	16
17	18	19	20	21	22	23
24	25	26	27	28	29	

March

S	M	T	W	T	F	S
						1
2	3	4	5	6	7	8
9	10	11	12	13	14	15
16	17	18	19	20	21	22
23	24	25	26	27	28	29
30	31					

Calendar N

April

S	M	T	W	T	F	S
		1	2	3	4	5
6	7	8	9	10	11	12
13	14	15	16	17	18	19
20	21	22	23	24	25	26
27	28	29	30			

May

S	M	T	W	T	F	S
				1	2	3
4	5	6	7	8	9	10
11	12	13	14	15	16	17
18	19	20	21	22	23	24
25	26	27	28	29	30	31

June

S	M	T	W	T	F	S
1	2	3	4	5	6	7
8	9	10	11	12	13	14
15	16	17	18	19	20	21
22	23	24	25	26	27	28
29	30					

Calendar N

July

S	M	T	W	T	F	S
		1	2	3	4	5
6	7	8	9	10	11	12
13	14	15	16	17	18	19
20	21	22	23	24	25	26
27	28	29	30	31		

August

S	M	T	W	T	F	S
					1	2
3	4	5	6	7	8	9
10	11	12	13	14	15	16
17	18	19	20	21	22	23
24	25	26	27	28	29	30
31						

September

S	M	T	W	T	F	S
	1	2	3	4	5	6
7	8	9	10	11	12	13
14	15	16	17	18	19	20
21	22	23	24	25	26	27
28	29	30				

Calendar N

October

S	M	T	W	T	F	S
			1	2	3	4
5	6	7	8	9	10	11
12	13	14	15	16	17	18
19	20	21	22	23	24	25
26	27	28	29	3	31	

November

S	M	T	W	T	F	S
						1
2	3	4	5	6	7	8
9	10	11	12	13	14	15
16	17	18	19	20	21	22
23	24	25	26	27	28	29
30						

December

S	M	T	W	T	F	S
	1	2	3	4	5	6
7	8	9	10	11	12	13
14	15	16	17	18	19	20
21	22	23	24	25	26	27
28	29	30	31			

Index